REVISE KEY STAGE 2 SATs
English

REVISION WORKBOOK

Above Expected Standard

Series Consultant: Janice Pimm

Authors: Helen Thomson

This revision workbook is written for students who aim to perform above the expected national standard in English in their Year 6 SATs.

For students who hope to perform at the expected standard, check out:

Revise Key Stage 2 SATs English Revision Guide:
Expected Standard   9781292146010

Revise Key Stage 2 SATs English Revision Workbook:
Expected Standard   9781292146003

For the full range of Pearson revision titles visit:
www.pearsonschools.co.uk/revise

 **P** Pearson

Contents

Grammar

Punctuation

Spelling

Writing

Reading

A small bit of small print

The Standards and Testing Agency publishes Sample Test Materials on its website. This is the official content and this book should be used in conjunction with it. The questions in *Now try this* have been written to help you practise every topic in the book. Remember: the real test questions may not look like this.

Introduction

About your tests

At the end of Year 6, you will take tests to find out about your English skills. This book will help you revise all of the important skills you need for your tests.

- There will be one **spelling** test. Your teacher will read 20 words out loud. You need to write down the correct spellings. This test will take about 15 minutes.

- There will be one **grammar** test. This test will ask you questions about spelling, punctuation and grammar. You will have 45 minutes to do this test.

- There will be one **reading** test. You will have to read three texts and answer questions about them. You will have 1 hour to do this test.

Your teacher will look at some of your pieces of **writing** but there won't be a writing test.

Using this book

Each page of this book is about a different skill. Use the checkboxes at the top of the page to track your progress:

Had a go   ☐   Tick this box when you've had a go at the page.

Nearly there   ☐   Tick this box when you understand the page quite well.

Nailed it!   ☐   Tick this box when you understand the page really well.

Pronouns

1. Circle all the pronouns in the sentences below.

   a) (She) met (him) at the station and then (they) caught the train to London.

   b) (Everyone) saw (them) running towards the bridge but
   (it) was too late to stop (them.)

   c) Neither of (us) realised what the time was.

   d) (He) wouldn't talk about (himself.)

   > Use pronouns in place of nouns so that you don't repeat the same nouns.

   4 marks

2. Rewrite the sentences below, replacing the underlined words with pronouns. One has been done for you.

   a) <u>Mrs Bosko</u> wasn't at school today.

   She wasn't at school today.

   b) I gave the book to <u>Juan</u>.

   I gave the book to him

   c) Michael drove <u>Amanda</u> to the airport.

   Michael drove her to the airport **2 marks**

3. Rewrite the passage below, replacing the nouns with pronouns where appropriate.

   Bashir and Jonathan set off for the bowling alley at five-thirty. The bus arrived at the stop at five-forty and Bashir and Jonathan got on the bus. Bashir and Jonathan were hoping to get to the bowling alley before six-thirty to make sure that Bashir and Jonathan got a game but when Bashir and Jonathan arrived Bashir and Jonathan were disappointed to find that the bowling alley was closed.

   I and him set off got the bowling
   alley at five-thirty. The bus
   attived at the stop at five sorty
   and I and him got on the bus.
   I and him

   5 marks

Noun phrases

1. **Underline the noun phrases in the sentences below.**

   a) The guitarist performing on stage was playing an old rock song.

   > Expanding noun phrases can make your writing more interesting and add detail.

   b) We went to the supermarket, which sells great ice-cream.

   c) The fat, floppy-eared puppy bounded towards its owner.

   d) At the concert hall we meet the boy with the spiky hair.

   e) The copper-edged mirror was above the fire place.

   5 marks

2. **Rewrite the sentences below, replacing the pronouns with expanded noun phrases. One has been done for you.**

   a) He was splashing in the rock pools.

   The boy wearing the striped shirt was splashing in the rock pools.

   b) They didn't have enough money to catch the tram.

   The boy didn't have enough money to catch the tram.

   c) It was sitting on the window ledge watching the birds.

   The cat was sitting on the window ledge watching the birds.

   d) Jackson delivered the pizza to them.

   Jackson delivered the Pizza to the family.

   e) Malak met her by the tennis courts.

   Malak met Joy by the tennis courts.

   f) She was walking towards us when it happened.

   Joy was walking towards Mario when she jumped.

   5 marks

2

Possessive pronouns

1. Circle the possessive pronouns in the sentences below.

 a) (Their) house has got a blue door.

 b) Those clothes by the door are (mine.)

 c) Most of the books are (hers.)

 d) (Your) father is really nice.

 e) Tom forgot (his) homework again.   **5 marks**

2. Rewrite the sentences below, replacing the noun and possessive apostrophe with a possessive pronoun. One has been done for you.

 a) Geraldine's brother broke his bicycle.

   Her brother broke his bicycle.

 b) The dog's collar was too big for it.

   The collar was too big for it.

 c) Selma replaced all of Freddy's chocolates.

   Selma replaced all of his chocolates.

 d) Grandfather's hips are causing him a lot of pain.

   His hips are causing him a lot of pain.

 e) Amita's car is brand new.

   Her car is brand new.   **4 marks**

3. Rewrite the sentence below, replacing the possessive pronoun with a noun and possessive apostrophe.

   His computer had been hacked.

   Mike's computer had been hacked.   **1 mark**

3

Determiners

1. Circle all the determiners in the sentences below. One has been done for you.

   a) (The seven) brown horses bolted through (that) gate.

   b) (Many people) attended his graduation ceremony.

   c) (A) new pupil arrived at school today, I met him in the sports hall.

   d) All (the) money was spent on her wedding.

   e) (This) is the best chicken I've ever tasted.

   A, and, the, every, this, th, many

   4 marks

> Determiners can make the noun more specific or more general.

2. Write two paragraphs describing a normal day at school. Include as many determiners as you can and underline each one.

   I woke up in the morning and ate my breakfast and went to school with everybody. I learn maths and english and had many education and come back home to study.

   6 marks

> Possessive pronouns such as 'Their' are also determiners. They show the ownership of the noun.

3. Rewrite the sentence below with determiners.

   We put cat in box, loaded into car and took to vet nearby.

   We put the cats in the box and and loaded them into the car and took them to a vet nearby.

   2 marks

Adjectives and adjectival phrases

1. Complete the sentences below by adding an appropriate adjective.

> An adjectival phrase is a group of words that gives more information about a noun or pronoun.

a) He was a very .... *friendly* *happy* boy and always smiling.

b) I always find it difficult to buy jeans that are long enough because

I am so ......*tall*...........................

c) The hurricane was ......*causing* *making*........ and caused considerable damage.   **3 marks**

2. Tick three boxes to show which sentences contain an adjectival phrase.

Tick **three**.

The train was going <u>faster and faster</u>.	☑
It is ten o'clock. ✗	☐
Those pancakes are extremely tasty.	☑
I prefer reading fiction to non-fiction.	☐
Scowling in anger, the man entered the room.	☑

3 marks

3. Underline the adjectival phrases in the sentences below.

a) I can't resist eating <u>delicious, triple-chocolate-coated</u> biscuits even though I know they aren't healthy.

b) The building on <u>the corner of the street</u> is about to collapse.   **2 marks**

4. Complete the sentences below with an appropriate adjectival phrase.

a) The woman, ..., is very kind.

b) Henry, ..., often arrives late.   **2 marks**

Verbs

1. Underline all the verbs in the following passage.

> Verbs are often called 'doing' words, but they can also describe what something is 'being'.

It was baking hot last weekend and so Xian and Nathanial decided to go to the beach. They both wanted to go kayaking so they made some enquiries about renting kayaks from the sailing shop. They managed to rent two kayaks for a reasonable price and buoyancy aids were also included at no extra cost. They paddled around the bay all afternoon. By the time they returned them to the shop their arms were aching badly.

"Shall we go again next weekend?" asked Xian.

"Yes, let's definitely do that, but only if the weather's good like today," replied Nathanial.

6 marks

2. Circle the correct form of the verb in the sentences below.

a) Sunita and I was/were really pleased when the holidays started.

b) I ain't/am not going to visit my grandmother this evening.

c) You were/was brilliant in the play.

d) Jacob haven't/hasn't been well this week.

1 mark

3. Tick the box that provides the best description of a verb.

Tick **one**.

a word used to describe a noun or pronoun ☐

a word used to talk about an action in the future ☐

a word used to talk about an action in the past, present or future ☐

a word used to describe something that is uncertain ☐

1 mark

Present and past tense

1. Tick one box below to show which sentence below is written in the past tense.

Tick **one**.

Alfred is the most elderly person in the village. ☐

Alfred is ninety-six years old. ☐

Alfred was born in 1920. ☐

Alfred is planning his next birthday party. ☐

1 mark

2. The passage below is written in the present tense. Rewrite it, putting it into the past tense.

> Khalid has two brothers and a sister. His sister has shoulder-length, brown hair and likes playing netball. She plays for her school team and is the captain. His brothers are identical twins and are two years younger than him. All the children in Khalid's family have inherited their mother's green eyes.

....

....

....

....

....

.... 5 marks

3. Look at the sentence below. Explain why the present tense is formed in two different ways.

Everyday Madeline catches the bus to school but this morning she is walking there with her friends.

....

.... 2 marks

7

Future tense

1. Tick three boxes to show which sentences express the future tense.

Tick **three.**

They're going to have salad and pizza for dinner this evening. ☐

The postman brought a parcel. ☐

The programme that you want to watch will be broadcast at seven o'clock. ☐

We're leaving for the airport soon. ☐

The car is being repaired in the garage. ☐

3 marks

2. Underline all the future tenses in the passage below.

> By the year 2030 it is predicted that cars will be engineered to enable commuters to fly to work along routes that will run above motorways. It is said that we are going to have a complete revolution in transportation. This will be brought about by the need for a radical solution to today's problems of road congestion and traffic. By the end of 2025 this situation is anticipated as being so acute that we will face gridlock on roads around our cities. Unless remedies are found the future will be very difficult for road transportation. A new plan is being formed and the government is launching this in three years' time.

3 marks

3. Write a paragraph about what you are going to do next week. Include as many examples as you can of the future tense.

....

....

....

....

.... 5 marks

Modal verbs

1. Underline the modal verb in each sentence below.

a) They would like to go to the wedding.

b) We shall see what happens next week.

c) If you go to America you must visit the Grand Canyon.

d) It may be a good idea to go fishing this afternoon.

> Modal verbs always come in front of another verb.

4 marks

2. Tick one box in each row to show how the modal verb affects the meaning of the sentence.

sentence	modal verb indicates certainty	modal verb indicates possibility
We will take the dog out when it stops raining.		
We may go on holiday to Tenerife.		
You should finish painting the steps before you go out.		
Sports day might be cancelled.		
He must call her today.		

5 marks

3. Draw lines to match each sentence with its correct possibility.

sentence

We might go to the party if we get back in time.

I will catch the ten o'clock bus.

Unless it stops raining the barbecue will be cancelled.

He will not be able to make it.

possibility

It will definitely happen.

It is unlikely to happen.

It definitely won't happen.

It might happen.

4 marks

Present and past perfect tense

1. Tick one box to show which sentence below is written in the past perfect tense.

Tick **one**.

We used to live in Wales. ☐

The timetable had begun before the new head teacher arrived. ☐

Hannah has taken the dog to the vets because it is ill. ☐

1 mark

2. Complete the sentences below, using either the present or past perfect tense.

a) The steam engine.. (invent) by 1700.

b) Be careful, the floor is wet because someone ....
(spill) their drink.

c) By the time we arrived all the seats..
(be taken).   **3 marks**

3. Write a sentence which contains an example of:

a) the present perfect tense

....

b) the past perfect tense.

.... **2 marks**

4. Tick the box that best describes when you should use the present perfect tense.

Tick **one**.

To talk about an event in the past that still has consequences now. ☐

To talk about a moment in the past and say that something was completed before then. ☐

To talk about an event in the past that is completely finished and not relevant now. ☐

1 mark

Future perfect tense

1. Tick the box that shows the sentence containing the future perfect tense.

Tick **one.**

> Use the future perfect tense to show the order in which events happen.

The concert will start as soon as the curtain goes up. ☐

Davit is going to clear out the shed this afternoon. ☐

By the time you are twelve years old you will have started secondary school. ☐

Jenny's new bicycle is arriving this afternoon. ☐

The supermarket has closed down. ☐

1 mark

2. Rewrite the sentences below, putting the verb into the correct form of the future perfect. One has been done for you.

a) Hopefully the package (deliver) in time for Christmas.

Hopefully the package will have been delivered in time for Christmas.
....

b) She wants to make sure the meal **(prepared)** before the guests arrive.

....

....

c) Ben **(complete)** the marathon before any of the other runners have started.

....

....

d) If he keeps eating so much junk food he **(become)** very fat before he grows up.

....

.... **4 marks**

3. Explain why we use the future perfect tense.

.... **1 mark**

11

Adverbs

1. Circle all of the adverbs in the passage below.

> Adverbs can describe 'when', 'how' or 'where' a verb is done. Most adverbs end in the suffix –ly but some don't, such as 'down'.

My brother has got a new, well-paid job and is working very hard. He gets up early in the morning and cycles very fast in order to get to the office before the rush-hour traffic. He works as a computer analyst. This involves carefully studying data and accurately cross-checking it to ensure that it has been input correctly. He loves his work and talks about it enthusiastically when he gets home. He will happily talk about it for hours.

4 marks

2. Write a review of your favourite film. Include at least one adverb to describe: a verb; an adverb; an adjective or a clause.

....

....

....

.... **4 marks**

3. Rewrite the sentences below, using adverbs to describe how these actions are completed. One has been done for you.

a) Faisel is a good singer.

   Faisel sings well.
   ....

b) Toby is a quiet speaker.

   ....

c) Caitlin is a beautiful painter.

   ....

d) Grandma is a bad sleeper.

   .... **3 marks**

Adverbial phrases

1. Underline the adverbial phrases in the sentences below.

> Adverbial phrases can describe **where**, **when**, **how** or **why** something happens.

a) We found our way by the light of the moon.

b) Before the end of the week, I will have completed the essay.

c) The dog chased the cat over the bridge.

d) So that I won't forget the date, I've put it in my diary.

e) Popcorn was sold during the interval.

f) I set my alarm, to make sure I woke up on time.

6 marks

2. Tick the three boxes that show sentences that contain fronted adverbials.

Tick **three**.

Out of the corner of my eye, I spotted the wallet. ☐

I ran there with a song in my heart. ☐

With great regret, the teacher announced that he was leaving. ☐

We found her hiding in a corner laughing. ☐

Speaking quickly, she explained what had happened. ☐

3 marks

3. Write your own sentence containing:

a) an adverbial phrase

....

....

b) a fronted adverbial phrase.

....

.... **2 marks**

13

Conjunctions

1. Underline all the conjunctions in the sentences below and say what type of conjunction they are. One has been done for you.

   a) I read a magazine <u>while</u> I waited for the train. subordinating conjunction

   b) I won't be happy again until I see you smile. ....

   c) We won't be able to play football today
   because the pitch is water-logged. ....

   d) The wallpaper is unusual but it is still pretty. ....

   3 marks

2. Rewrite the clauses below and join them with a conjunction.

   a) The bottle was empty ... we put it in the recycling bin.

   ....

   b) The puppy chews shoes ... it is still adorable.

   ....

   c) We arrived on time ... we left the house late.

   .... **3 marks**

3. Circle the subordinating conjunctions in the list below.

   after   because   but   and   so   when   while   although

   5 marks

4. Tick one box below to show which sentence is correct.

   Tick **one.**

   Subordinating conjunctions join together
   compound sentences. ☐

   Co-ordinating conjunctions join together two
   main clauses or compound sentences. ☐

   Co-ordinating conjunctions join together two
   complex sentences. ☐

   1 mark

Prepositions

1. Underline the preposition in each sentence below. One has been done for you.

   a) The bridge is <u>above</u> the river.

   b) They had dinner before they went out.

   c) The dentist is closed at the weekend.

   d) It is on the top shelf.

   e) The lions were running into the forest.   **4 marks**

2. Which of the sentences below contains a preposition of time, place or direction? Tick one box in each row.

   Some prepositions such as on are used in more than one category.

	time	place	direction
They were running towards the stadium.			
I found the briefcase behind the sofa.			
The orchestra played while we listened.			
The grandfather clock is beside the chest of drawers.			
The Second World War took place over seventy years ago.			
She peeped out between her fingers.			

   6 marks

3. Write three sentences, with the first one containing a preposition of time, the second a place and the third a direction. Remember to punctuate your answers correctly.

   ....

   ....

   ....

   .... **3 marks**

Prepositional phrases

1. Underline the prepositional phrases in the sentences below. One has been done for you.

   a) We camped <u>on the cliff top</u>.

   b) The car hurtled around the bend.

   c) They danced by the light of the moon.

   > Remember, a prepositional phrase is a group of words containing a preposition and usually a noun or pronoun.

   d) She passed her driving exam after many attempts.

   e) I had no idea, until this very day, that she was so intelligent.   **4 marks**

2. Do the sentences below contain a preposition of time, place or direction? Tick one box in each row.

	time	place	direction
They go away fishing over a long weekend.			
The aeroplane taxied along the narrow runway.			
That house, next to the one with the tall chimney, is his.			

   3 marks

3. Write three sentences, each containing a prepositional phrase of:

   a) time

   ....

   b) place

   ....

   c) direction.

   ....   **3 marks**

Subjunctive

1. Underline the subjunctive forms in the sentences below.

   a) It is essential that he complete the forms on time.

   b) The council demands that planning permission be approved prior to the work commencing.

   c) It is suggested that applicants undergo a health test.

   d) I demand that you apologise.

   e) He advises that she arrive after 1pm.

   f) Our teacher recommended that they check their notes.   **6 marks**

2. Rewrite these sentences, using the subjunctive form to make them sound more formal.

   a) Overweight patients should lose weight by following a sensible diet.

   b) You will do as I say!

   c) The weather is dreadful so please drive carefully.

   d) It's nearly tea-time so we should go home.

   e) He shouldn't come.   **5 marks**

   > You will use the subjunctive form mainly in formal language.

3. Write a sentence containing a subjunctive form.

   ....

   ....   **1 mark**

4. Explain when you would use the subjunctive.

   ....

   ....   **2 marks**

Questions

1. Tick three boxes to show which of these sentences are questions.

Tick **three.**

How could this possibly happen ☐
That teacher is very strict ☐
Would you prefer tomatoes or peppers with your steak ☐
She's quite tall, isn't she ☐
That's fantastic news ☐

3 marks

2. Complete the question tags in the sentences below.

a) It's terrible weather, ...?

b) She's a brilliant chess-player, ...?

c) Joe and Matias aren't very tidy, ...?

d) Mariam has got two brothers, ...?

4 marks

3. Write three questions, each using one of the question words 'who', 'what' and 'when'.

....

....

.... 3 marks

4. Write three questions using inversions.

....

....

.... 3 marks

Commands and exclamations

1. Are these sentences commands or exclamations? Tick one box in each row.

	command	exclamation
Stop throwing those stones immediately!		
What wonderful news that is!		
Take these files to the headmaster's office!		
How amazing that must be!		
Run as fast as you can!		

Exclamation marks often punctuate commands. Commands usually take the imperative verb form.

5 marks

2. Tick the sentences that are in the imperative form.

Tick **all** that apply.

What a gorgeous painting! ☐

Quick! Go and phone the police! ☐

I can't wait to see her again! ☐

Boil the rice for ten minutes then rinse it in hot water. ☐

Where is the city centre? ☐

2 marks

3. Exclamations must contain certain things.

a) Give two examples of what an exclamation must contain.

....

b) Explain why we use exclamation marks.

.... 2 marks

4. Write a sentence using the imperative form.

.... 1 mark

Subject and object

1. Underline the subject in each sentence below. One has been done for you.

   a) <u>Stephanie</u> drove the sports car.

   b) Yusif filled the shopping trolley.

   c) They hid the jewels in a cave.

   d) The wheel barrow left a trail of dirt.

   e) A cat walked through our garden.

   > The subject and object aren't always people. They can be things.

   4 marks

2. Circle the objects in the sentences below.

   a) Kaspar ate all the bread.

   b) He has taken the dog out.

   c) The rain is spoiling our day out.

   d) The cat has caught a mouse.

   e) Edwina loves cheese.

   f) The pen has leaked ink everywhere.

   6 marks

3. Write a sentence containing a subject, verb and object.

   ....

   .... **1 mark**

4. Tick the boxes to show what two things you need to make a complete sentence.

   Tick **two.**

   a subject   ☐
   a verb   ☐
   an object   ☐

   2 marks

Phrases and clauses

1. Are the sentence parts below phrases or clauses? Tick one box in each row.

	phrase	clause
On a dark stormy night,		
As he picked his way between the crowds,		
After a tremendous effort,		
Because they know it's wrong to pick the flowers,		
Without having all the information to hand,		

5 marks

2. Underline all the phrases in the sentences below.

   a) Until final completion, no one knows what it will look like.

   b) It lay there, broken into a thousand pieces.

   c) Before sitting the test, you need to revise.

   d) The car hurtled down the road and then, smoke pouring from its exhaust, it came to an abrupt stop.

A phrase is not a complete sentence. A clause has a subject that is actively doing something.

4 marks

3. Explain the difference between a phrase and a clause.

   ....

   .... 2 marks

4. Write a sentence containing:

   a) a clause

   ....

   b) a phrase.

   .... 2 marks

Main and subordinate clauses

1. Are the underlined clauses main clauses or subordinate clauses? Tick one box in each row.

> You can swap main and subordinate clauses around, and the sentence will still make sense.

	main	subordinate
<u>Although it was bitterly cold</u>, it still didn't snow.		
<u>Juma didn't come to school today,</u> because he has flu.		
While we were playing tennis, <u>my uncle made a video recording of the match.</u>		
The temperature is usually high in August, <u>although we still get some rainy days.</u>		

4 marks

2. Underline the subordinate clauses in the sentences below.

a) Since his dog died, Andrei has been quite depressed.

b) Jenny was drawing while she listened to the radio.

c) Ivona doesn't really like to exercise, even though she goes to the gym twice a week.

d) Despite the fact that he was very angry, he kept his emotions under control.

4 marks

3. Write a sentence containing a main and a subordinate clause.

....

.... 1 mark

4. Explain the difference between a main and a subordinate clause.

....

.... 2 marks

Compound and complex sentences

1. Are the sentences below compound or complex? Tick one box in each row. One has been done for you.

	compound	complex
I won't be able to carpet the floor until the bedroom has been decorated.		✓
Jozef was playing chess, while everyone else was watching television.		
I love cycling but I don't like swimming.		
England is part of Great Britain and it is also part of the United Kingdom.		
Despite being in awful pain, Josie completed the sponsored walk.		

4 marks

2. Complete each of the sentences below with an appropriate conjunction.

   a) They didn't wake up on time .... their alarm clock didn't ring.

   b) .... the family was impoverished they were still very contented.

   c) At the ice rink we learnt how to skate backwards .... do spins.

   d) Christophe loves Cheddar cheese .... he hates Stilton.

   4 marks

3. What is the name of the type of conjunction underlined in the sentence below?

   Claude bought a new DVD <u>but</u> Francois didn't have enough money.

   .... 1 mark

4. Tick two boxes to show which of these sentences are correct.

   Tick **two.**

   A complex sentence is formed by one main clause and one or more subordinate clauses. ☐

   A complex sentence is formed by two main clauses. ☐

   A compound sentence is formed by two main clauses connected by a coordinating conjunction. ☐

   2 marks

23

Relative clauses

1. Circle all the relative pronouns in the list of words below.

> A relative clause adds detail to a noun.

who   why   which   there   whosoever   the   that   whose

1 mark

2. Underline the relative clauses in the sentences below. One has been done for you.

   a) My American pen pal, <u>who lives in New York</u>, e-mails me every fortnight.

   b) The sports hall, which is securely locked after school, was broken into last night.

   c) My cousin, whose friend works in London, has invited me to her new house.

   d) The brightly-coloured parrot, which was squawking in the cage, is very tame.

   e) The wedding ceremony, when a date has been set, will be very elaborate.

   4 marks

3. Complete the sentences below with the correct relative pronoun.

   a) Our local MP, ... lives at the end of my road, represents our interests in Parliament.

   b) In Sri Lanka, ... you can go whale watching, the temperature can get very high.

   c) The shop, ... sells those delicious pies, is at the end of the street.

   d) My teacher, ... name is Mr Frederick, is very nice.

   4 marks

4. Write a sentence containing a relative clause.

   ....

   .... **1 mark**

Active and passive voice

1. Are the sentences below in the active or passive voice?
   Tick one box in each row.

	active	passive
Halim picked a bunch of flowers for his mother.		
The rubbish was cleared up by the environmentally conscious students.		
The books had been laid out on the table.		
Jerry is playing at a gig tonight.		
The party was held in the village hall.		

> The active and passive voice are two different ways of giving the same information. Choosing either an active or passive voice will change the tone of your writing.

5 marks

2. Rewrite the sentences below in the passive voice. One has been done for you

   a) Terry trimmed the hedge on Saturday.

   The hedge was trimmed by Terry.
   ....

   b) They left the luggage in the storage area.

   ....

   c) The post woman has delivered the parcel.

   ....

   d) The horses eat all the grass in the paddock.

   ....

   e) He is hanging the clothes on the line.

   .... 4 marks

3. Give two reasons why you would choose to use the passive voice.

   ....

   .... 2 marks

4. Write a sentence in the passive voice.

   .... 1 mark **25**

Standard English verbs

1. Tick two boxes to show which sentences are written in Standard English.

Tick **two.**

It is regrettable that he has chosen to ignore everyone's advice on this matter. ☐

That's wonderful news! I'm going to be an auntie. ☐

Everyone was hanging out at the recreation ground last night. ☐

Please ensure that all litter is collected and placed in the bins provided. ☐

> Use Standard English when you need to sound more formal.

2 marks

2. Rewrite the sentences below, using the correct subject to verb agreement. One has been done for you.

a) She ain't very tall.

She isn't very tall.

....

b) He were at school yesterday.

....

c) They was finishing their homework.

....

d) We was waiting in the queue.

.... **3 marks**

3. Tick two boxes to show in which of these situations you should use Standard English.

Tick **two.**

writing a letter to your local fire station to ask if your school could visit ☐

writing a thank you letter to your cousin for sending you a present ☐

applying for a Saturday job helping out in a pet shop ☐

> You might not use the correct subject to verb agreement in spoken language, but it's important when you are writing.

1 mark

Standard English tense and voice

1. a) Are these sentences written in the correct tense? Tick one box in each row.

	correct	incorrect
The bikes was left near the station.		
The plates were filled by the waiters as soon as they were empty.		
The television has been left on all day, wasting electricity.		
The lawn were mowed by the gardener.		

   b) Correct the incorrect sentences.

> Standard English often uses the passive voice in the past tense.

....

.... 6 marks

2. Rewrite the sentences below, putting the underlined verbs into the correct past tense form. One has been done for you.

   a) I <u>do</u> my homework yesterday.

   I did my homework yesterday.
   ....

   b) The church <u>is</u> built in 1786.

   ....

   c) The burgers <u>are</u> cooked to perfection in time for the barbecue.

   .... 2 marks

3. On a separate piece of paper, write a short note in Standard English to your teacher asking for an extra day's extension to complete your homework. Explain that the dog chewed it. Use at least one example of the passive tense.

4 marks

27

Standard English grammar

1. Tick two boxes to show which sentences are written in Standard English.

Tick two.

Me and my mate Joseph had an amazing time at the fairground. ☐

The concert is scheduled to commence at seven o'clock. ☐

He's brilliant at football, isn't he? ☐

We attended our grandmother's eightieth birthday celebration. ☐

That film is so cool! ☐

When you are writing In Standard English, avoid slang or dialect.

2 marks

2. Rewrite the sentences below in Standard English.

a) I finished my homework dead quick.

....

b) It was great to meet you!

....

c) Them peaches look yummy.

.... **4 marks**

3. Which of the letters below should be formal and which should be informal? Tick one box in each row.

	formal	informal
a letter to your friend planning a camping holiday		
a letter of complaint to a shop		

2 marks

4. Write a sentence in Standard English explaining that you and a friend are going to the cinema tomorrow.

.... **1 mark**

Commas for clarity

1. Read the sentences below, then add commas to clarify their meaning.

> Remember that without commas language can be ambiguous (unclear) or confusing.

a) The table was set with a buffet of jelly sausage rolls ice-cream burgers and walnut salad.

b) The teacher told us to put our bags under our desks take out our PE kit get changed and then line up outside the gym.

c) You need to pack a sleeping bag ground sheet a water bottle and warm clothes.

d) While you're at the shop buy bread cheese milk and a bunch of grapes.

4 marks

2. Punctuate the below sentences correctly.

> Commas are often used to separate main, subordinate and relative clauses.

a) Uncle Stanley who has worked at the factory for twenty-five years will retire soon.

b) Although it was very late the sky was still illuminated.

c) Mina who you met when we were skiing loves pasta.

d) Despite being quite small Nathaniel is very strong.

e) Even though you're not keen on cheese you should still try the pizza.

5 marks

3. Rewrite this sentence with the correct punctuation so that the meaning is clear.

I love eating my friends my grandmother and skate boarding.

.... **1 mark**

4. Give two reasons why it is important to use commas.

....

.... **1 mark**

Parenthesis

1. Tick the box to show which sentence is punctuated correctly.

Tick **one**.

The indoor market was a hive of activity, filled with people everywhere, with stalls piled high with goods for sale. ☐

The indoor market–was a hive of activity–filled with people everywhere with stalls piled high with goods for sale. ☐

The indoor market was a hive of activity filled with people everywhere (with stalls piled high with goods) for sale. ☐

> When identifying parentheses remember that the sentence would still make sense if you took out the words they enclose.

1 mark

2. Put brackets around the parentheses in these sentences.

a) Sajan who speaks three languages doesn't like maths.

b) The mirror which hangs above the fireplace is very old.

c) The beach where we spent the weekend had beautiful dunes.   **3 marks**

3. Complete the sentences below, adding your own information in the parentheses.

a) The bowling alley – .... – was always very popular.

b) Renee (...) had ambitions to be an actress.

c) Simon (...) has five brothers.

d) The old sofa – .... – needed replacing.

4 marks

4. Explain why we use parentheses.

....

.... **1 mark**

Colons

1. Tick one box below to show which sentence is punctuated correctly.

Tick **one.**

At the supermarket: we bought six eggs, half a kilo
of oranges, chocolate and ham. ☐

At the supermarket we bought, six eggs half a kilo of
oranges, chocolate and ham. ☐

At the supermarket we bought: six eggs, half a kilo
of oranges, chocolate and ham. ☐

At the supermarket we bought six eggs: half a kilo of
oranges, chocolate and ham. ☐

1 mark

2. Punctuate each of the sentences below with a colon and commas.

a) In my locker I keep extra pens books a bar of chocolate
and my rugby boots.

b) To train for a marathon you need to do warm-up
exercises run six miles a day and eat a healthy diet.

2 marks

3. Punctuate the sentences below correctly.

a) The television presenter announced We have just received the
breaking news that a spaceship with six Martians has landed on Earth.

b) Albert Einstein said Look deeper into nature and
then you will understand everything better.

2 marks

4. Write two sentences:

a) one that contains a colon to introduce a list.

> The items
> in the list still need
> to be separated
> by commas.

....

....

b) one that contains a colon to introduce a quotation.

....

.... 2 marks

Semi-colons

1. Tick two boxes to show which of these sentences are correctly punctuated.

Tick **two**.

Nathan has been working out every day; he's getting very fit now. ☐

The hurricane caused tremendous damage: broken windows; dislodged tiles; up-rooted trees; disconnected power lines and the destruction of gardens. ☐

> Remember, colons and semi-colons look very similar but are used in different ways.

Nathan; has been working out every day, he's getting very fit now. ☐

The hurricane caused tremendous damage; broken windows, dislodged tiles, up-rooted trees, disconnected power lines and the destruction of gardens. ☐

2 marks

2. Punctuate these sentences with colons and semi-colons.

a) The garden is filled with a huge variety of plants exquisite trailing roses lilac-blossomed wisteria scarlet hibiscus and wild foxgloves.

> The two clauses must give information about the same topic.

b) The wildlife safari park keeps many different types of interesting animals red wolves roaring lions Siberian tigers lively-eyed lemurs and long-limbed giraffes.

c) She is a huge fan of that pop star she has an extensive collection of his music.

3 marks

3. Tick one box to show why semi-colons have been used in the sentence below.

There are a lot of things you can do at the beach when the weather is nice: swim in the sea; play football; play volleyball; go snorkelling or just lie in the sun.

Tick **one**.

To show the beginning of a sentence. ☐

To show the middle of a sentence. ☐

To separate items in a long list. ☐

To introduce a new clause. ☐

1 mark

Possessive apostrophes

1. Tick the box to show which of these sentences is correctly punctuated.

Tick **one.**

> Possessive apostrophes are used to show that something belongs to someone or something.

The womens' toilet has beautiful porcelain hand basins and scented soap. ☐

The women's toilet has beautiful porcelain hand basins and scented soap. ☐

The womens toilet has beautiful porcelain hand basins and scented soap. ☐

1 mark

2. Rewrite the sentences below, inserting possessive apostrophes. One has been done for you.

   a) Sophies laptop has a green case.

   Sophie's laptop has a green case.
   ....

   b) The childrens entertainer was very funny.

   ....

   c) The boys cloakroom is on the ground floor.

   ....

   d) Toms jeans are in the tumble dryer.

   .... **3 marks**

3. Rewrite the sentences below, using possessive apostrophes. One has been done for you.

   a) The pots belonging to Darnel are fragile.

   Darnel's pots are fragile.
   ....

   b) The sweatshirt belonging to Herbert is filthy.

   ....

   c) The driveway of our neighbours is close to ours.

   ....

   d) The car owned by Jamal is very smart.

   ....

   e) The school the children attend is in the centre of town.

   .... **4 marks**

33

Apostrophes for contractions

1. Tick the box to show which sentence is correctly punctuated.

Contraction is shortening words to reflect how we speak. An apostrophe is used to replace the letters which are omitted (left out).

Tick **one.**

She has'nt visited Scotland for four years. ☐

She hasn't visited Scotland for four years. ☐

She hasnt visited Scotland for four years. ☐

1 mark

2. Rewrite the sentences below using contractions. One has been done for you.

a) She is a highly skilled technician.

She's a highly skilled technician.
....

b) We have not lived here for long.

....

c) It is convenient that the bus leaves from the end of our street.

.... 2 marks

3. Rewrite the sentences below extending the contractions.

a) He hasn't been able to spare the time to complete the form.

....

b) They wouldn't accept this proposal under any circumstances.

.... 2 marks

4. Write the contractions of the words listed below.

It will ....

could not ....

they are ....

can not .... 2 marks

Direct speech

1. Tick one box to show which of the sentences is punctuated correctly.

"where have all the apricots gone," asked Deanna. ☐

"Where have all the apricots gone? asked Deanna. ☐

"Where have all the apricots gone?" asked Deanna. ☐

"where have all the apricots gone?" asked Deanna. ☐

> You must punctuate with speech marks to show the actual words spoken in direct speech.

1 mark

2. Rewrite the sentences below as direct speech. Remember to punctuate your answers correctly. One has been done for you.

a) Please accompany the parking attendant to the ticket office said the man in uniform

"Please accompany the parking attendant to the ticket office," said the man in uniform.

b) We've won the competition shouted Donal

....

c) Does it ever stop raining in this country asked Bridget gloomily

....

d) Help all the chickens have escaped

.... **3 marks**

3. Two people are planning a trip to the beach. Write a paragraph recording their conversation, using direct speech.

....

....

....

....

.... **5 marks**

Bullet points

1. Are these statements in the table true or false? Tick one box in each row.

	true	false
Bullet points should always be used in direct speech.		
A lead-in phrase is usually used to introduce a bullet list.		
We use bullet points to organise information into a list.		
Bullet points cannot be used in written instructions.		

Bullet points are used to organise information into a list.

4 marks

2. Rewrite the sentence below, using bullet points and the correct punctuation.

In order to fully qualify as a doctor you need to: be interested in biology, gain high grades at school, study at university for five years, work long hours in hospitals while you are training

....

....

....

....

....

.... 4 marks

3. Write a list of bullet points to describe the qualities needed to be a good teacher. Include a lead-in clause and make at least four bullet points.

....

....

....

....

....

.... 4 marks

Hyphens and ellipses

1. Do the sentences in the table contain hyphens or ellipsis?
   Tick one box in each row.

	hyphen	ellipsis
It was a spine-chilling thriller.		
The audience held their breath as the curtain finally lifted and the singer walked onto the stage, she opened her mouth to sing and...		
The deep-fried fritters were very greasy.		
James loves wind-surfing and does it every weekend.		

Be careful not to confuse hyphens with dashes. Hyphens are shorter and are used differently.

4 marks

2. Insert hyphens in the correct places in the sentences below.

   a) We drove down the one way street.

   b) Ready made meals are often expensive and sometimes unhealthy.

   c) Although Kara is left handed she paints with her right hand.

   d) The red hot curry was delicious even though it made my eyes water.   **4 marks**

3. Tick two boxes to explain how ellipses are used.

   Tick **two.**

   To join two clauses together. ☐

   To show a word or extra text has been left out. ☐

   To show a pause or change of direction. ☐

   To create suspense in a piece of writing. ☐

   2 marks

Prefixes

1. Draw lines to match each root word with the correct prefix. One has been done for you.

in
dis
un
im
ir
mis

behave
mature
regular
respectful
qualified
correct

5 marks

2. Complete the sentences, using the correct prefix.

   a) It is .... fortunate that they lost their bags while on holiday.

   b) If I don't pass the exam this time I will .... take it next month.

   c) The walkway provides pedestrians with access to the other side of the road through a .... way.

   d) It is very .... responsible to drive too fast.

   e) If we are quick we will catch the .... views of the other films.

   5 marks

3. Write three nouns that contain prefixes.

   ....

   3 marks

4. Tick one box to show how prefixes are used.

   Tick **one.**

   To make a root word sound more interesting. ☐

   To change the meaning of a root word. ☐

   To give a root word its opposite meaning. ☐

   1 mark

Suffixes

1. **Underline all the words containing suffixes in the text below.**

   My eldest brother Tim has started taking driving lessons. My mother is nervous about this but Tim assured her that he is a very careful driver. His instructor is a cheerful man who wears brightly coloured ties.

   > A suffix is a letter, or group of letters that you add to the end of a word to change its meaning.

   5 marks

2. **Complete the sentences, using the root word in brackets with a suffix. One has been done for you.**

   a) The kittens are very (play).

   The kittens are very playful.
   ....

   b) He is very (care) and his writing is full of mistakes.

   ....

   c) There was nothing she could do to help so she felt completely (hope).

   ....

   d) He is a kind and generous-hearted man and I am full of (admire) for him.

   ....

   e) It would be (advantage) to get there early to make sure we get a seat.

   .... **4 marks**

3. **Draw lines to match each root word with the correct suffix to form a new word.**

   root word   suffix

sudden		ous
comfort		ment
content		ly
danger		able

   4 marks

39

Synonyms and antonyms

1. Draw lines to match each word in the left column with the correct antonym. One has been done for you.

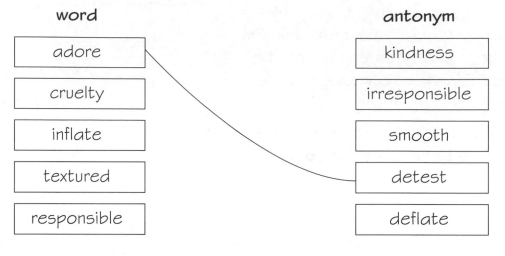

word

antonym

word	antonym
adore	kindness
cruelty	irresponsible
inflate	smooth
textured	detest
responsible	deflate

4 marks

2. Rewrite these sentences, choosing a synonym to replace each underlined word.

a) The new multi-screen cinema is <u>very big</u>.

....

b) The pizzas were <u>very tasty</u>.

....

c) He <u>gazed</u> out of the window at the trees.

....

d) It is normal to feel <u>anxious</u> about starting a new school.

....   4 marks

3. Circle two words in the text that are synonyms.

Charley and Dean have been close friends since their first day at school. They have always got on well and rarely quarrel. Even when they occasionally argue they always make up again quickly.

1 mark

Tricky spellings: silent letters

1. Circle the words with silent letters in the text below.

> A good way to check whether a letter is silent is to pronounce all the letters in a word. If it doesn't sound right you will spot the silent letters.

I love exploring the countryside in Spring, especially if I can pat the lambs. Last Tuesday we took a bus from the centre of the city and headed out into the countryside. When we got off we climbed up the hill towards the castle where we rested for a while. My friend Christof said that he had heard that the castle was haunted by a ghost. I knew that wasn't true and it made me laugh. Christof has a knack of making me laugh. We went down the lane and found some lambs but when I tried to pat them the mother sheep knocked me over! A little man who looked like a gnome came running towards us, shaking his fist and baring his knuckles. It was the farmer! We ran off!

8 marks

2. Complete the table below. Add two words containing the same spelling pattern. One has been done for you.

knock	wrist	chemist	where
	wrong		

4 marks

3. Write a sentence that includes two words containing silent letters.

....

....   **2 marks**

Tricky spellings: pronunciation

1. Complete the table with five sets of 'ie' and 'ei' words that are pronounced as 'ee' (as in tree). Two have been done for you.

> The most common ways to spell the 'ee' sound are 'ee', 'ea' and 'y'. For example flee, meat, ley.

ei	ie
receive	achieve

4 marks

2. Write two words containing the 'ough' grapheme that rhyme with the word 'port'.

> Graphemes are letters which make a single sound.

....

....

2 marks

3. Underline five words in this text that are spelled incorrectly and correct the spellings.

David, the cheef of police, recieved a medal at the Town Hall for his bravery. The room had a large, painted ceiling and the mayor siezed his hand in a warm handshake. Although the meeting was breif, David felt that this was a great acheivement and an experience he wouldn't forget.

....

....

....

....

.... 5 marks

Homophones and homonyms

1. Circle the correct homophone to complete each of the sentences below.

> Homophones and homonyms are pairs of words that sound the same but have **different** meanings.

a) The toddlers ran across the sand in <u>bare / bear</u> feet.

b) My uncle didn't have enough money to buy the car so he took out a bank <u>lone / loan</u>.

c) Before the Internet all communications were by the <u>mail / male</u> postal service.

d) The children believed that Santa was arriving in a <u>slay / sleigh</u> pulled by reindeer.

e) His ears were blocked and he couldn't <u>hear / here</u> the birdsong.   **5 marks**

2. Rewrite the sentences below. Use the underlined homonym to write a new sentence that uses the alternative meaning. One has been done for you.

a) After walking along the beach we bought fish and <u>chips</u>.

The old paintwork is hard to remove so Aadesh <u>chips</u> away at it with a chisel.
....

b) We put an extra <u>coat</u> of varnish on the woodwork.

....

c) Khalid put a rubber <u>band</u> around the papers to secure them.

....

d) There's no hurry so let's just <u>coast</u> along at relaxing speed.

....

e) The lawyer put in a <u>counter</u>-claim on behalf of her client.

.... **4 marks**

3. Explain the difference between a homonym and a homophone.

....

.... **2 marks**

43

Audience and purpose

1. Draw lines to match the description of the text with its most likely audience.

> Remember, 'audience' means the people who will read the text and 'purpose' means the reason it was written.

text

advice on travelling to Japan
instructions to assemble flat-pack furniture
a science fiction novel
a history textbook

audience

a school pupil
a tourist
a customer of a DIY store
someone who likes stories about space and time travel

4 marks

2. Read the passage below. Explain the intended audience and its purpose.

> The waves were pounding the shore like mighty warriors storming a citadel of sand, and as the storm raged they grew taller and fiercer, battering the beach with violent assaults. Each attack slapped and dragged the shore under its relentless battering.
>
> Megan huddled inside her woollen cloak, clutching the edges in her battle to prevent the angry wind from tearing it away and leaving her exposed to the cruel elements. Her bare feet were numb with cold inside her wooden clogs. She peered out to the horizon to where her father's wooden ship was being tossed and shaken on the waves like a toy boat.

....

.... 2 marks

3. On a separate piece of paper, write a paragraph to be published in a tourist office brochure in your home town. The purpose of the text is to advise visitors and suggest local attractions in your town.

5 marks

Planning and organising

1. Write down two important things you need to think about when planning a piece of text.

> To produce well written text it is really useful to make a plan of what you are going to say.

....

.... 2 marks

2. Plan a short fictitious story. Use the organiser below to plan your writing.

Title
Introductory paragraph
Main section
Conclusion

8 marks

3. Use the notes in your organiser above to write the story on a separate piece of paper.

8 marks

Drafting and improving

1. Give examples of three literary devices that writers use to improve their writing.

> Draft and improve your writing to make sure you get the best possible result.

....

....

....

3 marks

2. Read the passage below. Rewrite it to make the story more amusing and interesting. Add your own ending. Remember to use correct punctuation.

> In the second draft, use literary devices such as **adjectives**, **alliteration**, **similes** and **imagery** to improve the text and make it more interesting.

Tanya's mum was working late so she asked Tanya to make supper for herself and her younger brother Nathanial. Tanya didn't like cooking and wasn't very good at it. There was only one dish she knew how to make and that was beans on toast, but Daniel didn't want beans on toast, he wanted spaghetti bolognaise. Tanya and Daniel walked to the supermarket to buy the ingredients for spaghetti bolognaise. They bought: mincemeat, a packet of spaghetti, tomato sauce and onions. When they got home Tanya put the ingredients on the table and then she started to cook. She burned the mincemeat and over-boiled the spaghetti.

....

....

....

....

....

.... **5 marks**

3. Give three reasons why writers often do several drafts before they complete a text.

.... **3 marks**

Proof-reading

1. Rewrite and improve the passage below. Check for errors in punctuation and spelling. Make sure that you correct all the errors.

> Proof-reading means checking for spelling and punctuation errors. You should also look for ways to make the text more engaging.

The Secret Maze

Me and my dad visited a big, stately home in the contryside at the wekend. As we drove up a enormous long driveway the impressive, manor house came into view. Dad park the car in the car park

"which part of the house would you like to see first " asked Dad. "theres a lot to see."

"Lets explore the garden, I replied.

So we set off to look round the grounds. There was a huge lawn with marble fountan in the centre. The lawn was surrounded by flower beds and shrubs tended by a hole team of gardeners. They was busy weeding planting and watering the planets.

We were walking along a little pathway around the edje of lawn when dad spoted a stone archway.

"I wonder where that leeds to!" he exclaimed.

"let's go and find out, I replied.

we went thrugh the archway and suddenly we were surrounded by tall hedgerows on all sides. We was lost in a maze

....

....

....

....

....

....

....   10 marks

2. List five types of error in the passage above.

....   5 marks

47

Writing stories

1. Write down four examples of how a writer can attract and keep their audience interested.

   > Remember that the purpose of fiction is to entertain the reader and make them want to read more.

   .... **4 marks**

2. Read the passage below and identify four ways in which the writer makes the story interesting.

   The Vaporised Teacher

   No one ever found out what happened to Mrs Smith. It was only the second week of term and our form teacher Mr Alexander was already off sick. 'Stress-related' or so the rumours went, at least that's what that Mark Watson from form 3b said he had heard whispered between the other staff. Mark was a real eavesdropper. He would sneak around like a cat sniffing out fish in a bin.

   Mrs Smith had been sent by the supply teaching agency. She was slim lady with a gentle face. We were only thirty minutes into the third period when she walked into the store cupboard and never came out. We all waited ten minutes, silent for once, a classroom of mice. Then Jude went in to have a look, but she'd gone! Just vaporised, a ghost of a teacher vanished out of the storeroom wall.

   ....

   ....

   ....

   .... **4 marks**

3. Write the opening two paragraphs of a short story on a separate piece of paper, using the devices you have identified above. Remember, your purpose is to interest your audience and make them want to read more.

   > Remember to use the correct punctuation in your writing.

   4 marks

Persuasive writing

1. Give one example of a type of text that uses persuasive writing.

   ....

   > Remember that the purpose of persuasive writing is to persuade the reader to do something.

   1 mark

2. Tick three boxes to show the main features of persuasive writing.

   provides instructions ☐

   uses emotive language ☐

   entertains the reader ☐

   has an opening sentence that hooks the reader ☐

   provides a historical account ☐

   has a catchy title ☐

   3 marks

3. Write a piece of persuasive text to persuade people to visit the town you live in.

   ....

   ....

   ....

   ....

   ....

   ....

   .... 5 marks

Instructions and reports

1. Tick the box to show which sentence is an example of an instructional text or a report.

Tick **one.**

The chill wind sighed through the gravestones like a ghost's breath. ☐

She sells seashells on the seashore. ☐

The match was scheduled to commence at two o'clock. ☐   **1 mark**

2. Read the conversation below. Use the factual information from the conversation to write a report of the match.

> The **imperative** and **bullet points** are common in this type of writing.

"How did the match go last Saturday?"

"Not very well, we were beaten 2–8 by Northcourt School."

"But, Shore Primary usually beats Northcourt! What went wrong?"

"Well Aliyah Thomson who plays wing-attacker twisted her ankle and had to leave before the end of the first quarter."

"That was bad luck. Who was goal-shooter?"

"Keiko Phillips. Northcourt have got a new player in goal-defence, Phoebe Williams, and she's really good."

"When are you due to play them again?"

"Not until April 22nd, at least we'll have plenty of time to train."

....

....

....

....

.... **5 marks**

3. Write instructions for something you do often. For example, making your bed or cooking a meal you know how to prepare.

....

.... **4 marks**

Formal letters

1. Tick four boxes below to show which phrases and sentences are suitable for inclusion in a formal letter.

Tick **four.**

Lots of love x ☐

Yours sincerely ☐

I look forward to hearing from you at your earliest convenience. ☐

If the manager were able to meet me that would be very valuable. ☐

It will be great to see you again. ☐

Please give my kind regards to your father. ☐

4 marks

2. Write a formal letter to the Prime Minister asking the government to fund a new sports hall in your town. Explain the reasons why it is needed and set out the letter correctly.

Use Standard English and include examples of the passive and subjective if appropriate.

Your letter should include the Prime Minister's address in the correct position on the page: **The Houses of Parliament, Westminster, London SW1A OAA.**

....

....

....

....

....

....

....

....

....

....

.... **6 marks**

51

Informal letters

1. Are these statements about informal letters true or false? Tick one box in each row.

> We use an informal style when we write to family and friends. Informal letters still need to be set out properly.

When writing informal letters you:	true	false
usually use formal or Standard English		
use 'chatty' language		
don't have to use correct spelling and punctuation		
don't have to include your address		

4 marks

2. Write an informal letter to an aunt or uncle giving them family news and inviting them to a party.

> Remember, you still need to follow rules to set out an informal letter.

....

....

....

....

....

....

....

....

....

....

.... **6 marks**

Reading skills: close meaning

Read the following passage and then answer the questions.

> **Stay where you are and then leave**
>
> "Alfie," she said. "I thought I'd let you sleep in. You had a big day yesterday"…
>
> "Where's Dad?" asked Alfie.
>
> "He's gone out."
>
> "Gone out where?"
>
> "Oh, I don't know," she said, unable to look him in the eye….
>
> Which Alfie knew wasn't true, because every afternoon when his father came home from the dairy, he told Margie every single detail of his day…, and then they sat there laughing while he explained how Bonzo Daly had left half a dozen churns outside in the yard… Or how Mr Asquith had done the poo to end all poos outside Mrs Fairfax from number four's house and her a direct descendant (she claimed) of the last Plantagenet King of England and meant for better places than Damley Road.

1. What time of day is it? Give evidence to support your answer.

   .... 2 marks

2. Which words in the following extract from the passage suggest Alfie doesn't believe Mrs Fairfax?

   '…Mrs Fairfax from number four's house and her a direct descendant (she claimed) of the last Plantagenet King of England…'

   .... 1 mark

3. Why do you think Alfie's mother is described as:

   'unable to look him in the eye'?

   .... 1 mark

4. What inference about Damley Road could you make from this quote?

   '…and meant for better places than Damley Road.'?

   .... 2 marks

Reading skills: the whole text

Read the following passage and answer the questions.

Stay where you are and then leave (Part 2)

"Do you think Dad will take me on the float with him tomorrow?" asked Alfie.

"Did you ask him?"

"Yes, but he said I couldn't until I was older."

…

Before Margie could answer, the door opened and, to Alfie's astonishment, a soldier marched in. He was tall and well built, the same size and shape as Alfie's dad, but he looked a little sheepish… But why would a solider just walk into their living room? he wondered…. Alfie realised that this wasn't just any soldier…

It was Georgie Summerfield.

It was his dad.

And that was when Margie dropped her knitting on the floor, put both hands to her mouth… before running from the room and up the stairs while Georgie looked round… and shrugged his shoulders.

"I had to," he said finally. "You can see that, Mum, can't you? I had to."

"We're finished," said Granny Summerfield, … turning away from her son as she looked out of the window, where more young men were walking… wearing uniforms just like Georgie's. "We're all finished."

---

1. On a separate sheet of paper, write a summary of the text.   3 marks

2. Explain Margie's reaction to the soldier.

   ....

   .... 2 marks

3. Compare the moods of the four characters in the text. How are they different?

   ....

   ....

   .... 4 marks

Fiction text

This is an extract from *Stolen Destinies* by Helen Thomson. The story is set in Oman in 1959 as a young doctor, James McRae, takes up a post at the British Consulate in Muscat and finds a country very different from the one he has left behind.

Muscat, Oman 1959

Whenever I look back on my arrival in Muscat I always recall the smell of spices. Long before I caught sight of land, more than two hours before the ramparts of rock emerged from the vanilla haze and the dreamscape of turrets and towers rose from the sea. I was greeted by the aroma of cardamom, cinnamon, sandalwood, frankincense and tantalising whiffs of others for which I had yet no name. There wasn't even a strong off-shore breeze. The torpid sea stretched sleepily to the horizon. Its satin surface was undisturbed but for the ship's marbled wake and the indolent wind had barely enough breath to fatten the dhow's sail.

Had I realised how far this journey would take me would I still have embarked? Had I known that having once set foot on the burning rocks of that enchanted land I was starting a voyage from which there could be no return? It is a question I sometimes ask myself these desolate days. When I look back at that hot-headed, young man and the path I chose. Now I'm approaching bitter, winter years and have little left in any worldly sense. No home as such, no loving wife or garden of neatly tended flower beds. All the comforts most men of my age and professional standing take for granted by the time, swept away on the tide of fate. It was an undercurrent too strong for me to ever have swum against. But in my heart I know the answer. Even if all I have left of this lifetime are these memories I would not barter these tender treasures for Jason's Golden Fleece.

"Muscat, first you smell then you see." The dhow's captain Ahmed stood at the stern, the rudder resting lightly in his calloused hands. He seemed to have an uncanny ability to read my thoughts.

"Yes, but where's the coast? We're still miles off?" Ahmed broke into his by now familiar croaky laugh and reached up to slap me painfully across my sun-blistered shoulders. I winced, for such a slightly built chap he was very strong and after ten days at sea on the open dhow my Celtic skin was raw.

He chuckled showing his yellowing teeth, what was left of them anyway, and held up two gnarled fingers. "We arrive in Muttrah two hours, *inshallah.*"

Muttrah, Muscat's commercial port, my pulse quickened. I'd been waiting for this moment for months. Within two hours we would disembark in the ancient land of Mazoon.

From these shores the Queen of Sheba had dispatched ships heavy with frankincense. The legendary lost city of Ubar was said to lie beneath the shifting sands of the Empty Quarter to the south. 'The Atlantis of the Sands' was how it had been described by Lawrence of Arabia. He had also dreamt of finding this ancient trading capital. I drifted into a familiar fantasy. Fabulous hoards of jewels and artefacts from three continents bought back by the frankincense merchants, lying untouched for over two thousand years. Never mind Lawrence of Arabia, I would be the one to unearth Ubar and its treasures. Ahmed broke into my daydreaming with another stinging slap.

"British Consulate very nice place. Good, soft bed for you tonight."

I must admit I hadn't given much thought to what my life at the British Consulate would be like. I'd been so wrapped up in the thrilling prospect of exploring Oman's uncharted terrain that I hadn't considered what life would be like as the personal physician to His Highness Bin Taimur, Sultan and absolute ruler of the Kingdom of Muscat. I was also to be the resident doctor to the small band of consular staff. Of what my professional duties would consist I knew very little. Some of my medical reference books were stuffed under crumpled shirts in the bottom of my worn leather hold-all beneath the deck. The rest were to follow by shipment. I didn't think I needed them anyway. I was only a few years out of university and thought I knew it all.

Ahmed passed me the goatskin water bag and I drank greedily. The tepid liquid slopped down my stubbly chin.

"Good?"

I solemnly nodded my appreciation, even though it tasted like ditchwater, I was genuinely grateful and Ahmed grinned again. He was the only one of the six-man crew with a smattering of English and he helped me get used to the local dialect.

Retrieving information

Read the extract from *Stolen Destinies* on pages 55 and 56 and then answer the following questions.

> A narrator is the character who is telling the story.

1. Was the sea calm or stormy on the day the narrator arrived in Muscat? Give two examples from the text to support your answer.

   ....

   .... 3 marks

2. How did the narrator (James McRae) first know that they were approaching the land?

   ....

   .... 1 mark

3. What is the narrator's profession?

   .... 1 mark

4. Tick the box correctly describing how much the narrator knows about his new job in Muscat.

   Tick **one**.

   He knows about it in great detail.   ☐

   He knows quite a lot.   ☐

   He knows hardly anything at all.   ☐   1 mark

5. What precious fragrance was once traded in and exported from Muscat, according to the text?

   .... 1 mark

Recording information: selecting an answer

Read the extract from *Stolen Destinies* on pages 55 and 56 and then answer the following questions.

> Some reading questions will ask you to choose an answer, or answers, from a selection of options. You might be asked to circle, underline or tick the correct answer.

1. Circle two words that best describe Ahmed's character.

    friendly   mean   intuitive   stubborn   **1 mark**

2. Tick the box correctly describing how old the narrator is when he is telling the story.

    > Be careful with these questions as it's easy to make a mistake and circle or tick the wrong box.

    Tick **one**.

    a young man   ☐

    a boy   ☐

    an old man   ☐

    1 mark

3. Read the statements below. Are they true or false?
    Tick one box in each row. One has been done for you.

	true	false
The narrator is now a very rich man.		✓
The narrator is sun-burned after his sea voyage.		
The narrator is going to spend another night sleeping on the dhow.		

    2 mark

4. Underline the adjective that best describes the narrator's feelings on arriving in Muscat.

    depressed   worried   excited   bored   indifferent   **1 mark**

Recording information: free answers

Read the story extract from *Stolen Destinies* on pages 55 and 56 and then answer the following questions.

> Some test questions will ask you to write your answer on lines or in a box. This might be a few words, a phrase or sentences.

1. Which words towards the end of page 55 tell you that the narrator has not shaved for several days?

   .... 1 mark

2. Does the narrator regret his choices in life? Explain your answer.

> The number of lines and the size of the space provided suggests how long your answer should be.

   ....

   ....

   .... 2 marks

3. Explain what the phrases 'desolate days' and 'winter years' tell us about the narrator's present situation and feelings as he reflects on his younger self.

   ....

   .... 2 marks

4. Describe what sort of person you think the narrator is. Give evidence to support your answer.

   ....

   ....

   .... 3 marks

Using evidence

Read the extract from Stolen Destinies on pages 55 and 56 and then answer the following questions.

1. **What do you think the climate is like in Muscat? Use evidence from the text to support your answer.**

   > To answer this type of question you need to locate the exact words and phrases that give you the information.

   .... **2 marks**

2. **Is the narrator married? Which words in the text tell you this?**

   .... **2 marks**

3. **a) Tick the box that best describes the narrator's impression of Oman on his arrival.**

   Tick **one**.

   densely populated   ☐

   a remote and undiscovered land   ☐

   a tourist destination   ☐
                                         1 mark

   b) Give evidence from the text to support your answer.

   .... **1 mark**

4. **How is Muscat ruled? Give evidence from the text to support your answer.**

   ....

   .... **2 marks**

5. **Find and copy evidence from the text that demonstrates the fact that Oman has an interesting history.**

   ....

   .... **2 marks**

Inference

Read the extract from Stolen Destinies on pages 55 and 56 and then answer the following questions.

1. **a)** Is Ahmed an old or young man?

   ....

   b) Which words tell you this?

   Some questions in your reading test will ask you to work out the answer through hints and clues. This is called inference.

   ....   **3 mark**

2. **What is the main reason that the narrator has come to Oman? Give evidence to support your answer.**

   The writer may use descriptions of facial expressions, actions and sounds to hint to the reader.

   ....

   .... **2 marks**

3. How can you tell that Ahmed and the narrator are of a different height?

   ....

   .... **2 marks**

4. Does the dhow have modern dining and storage equipment? Give evidence to support your answer.

   ....

   .... **2 marks**

Prediction

1. Re-read the extract below. What do you think will happen to make the narrator look back on his education like this?

> 'Some of my medical reference books were stuffed under crumpled shirts in the bottom of my worn, leather hold-all beneath the deck. The rest were to follow by shipment. I didn't think I needed them anyway. I was only a few years out of university and thought I knew it all.'

Some questions in the reading test will ask you to say what you think might happen next. The questions will ask you to use evidence from the text to support your prediction.

....

....

.... 2 marks

2. Will the narrator ever leave Muscat or Oman? Use evidence from the text to support your answer.

....

....

.... 2 marks

3. Do you think Ahmed and the narrator will remain friends? Use evidence from the text to support your answer.

....

....

.... 2 marks

Authors' language

Read the extract from Stolen Destinies on pages 55 and 56 and then answer the following questions.

1. What effect is the writer trying to convey in her choice of the word 'indolent' to describe the wind and her description of the sea as 'stretching sleepily'?

> Some questions in the test ask you to comment on how the writer's choice of words enhance the meaning.

....

.... 2 marks

2. What is the name of the literary device the writer uses when she selects these words?

.... 1 mark

3. Find and copy a phrase from page 55 that tells you that the narrator was very excited about arriving in Muscat.

....

.... 1 mark

4. What image does the writer convey in the phrase 'ramparts of rock'?

....

.... 1 mark

5. What is the name of the literary device used in the phrase 'ramparts of rock'?

.... 1 mark

Non-fiction text

The civilisation of Egypt was already ancient when the period known as the New Kingdom began. The kings of the New Kingdom built an empire in north-east Africa and the Middle East.

The Roots of the Empire

By around 3000 BCE, small settlements had grown up along the banks of the Nile River, which was the lifeblood of Egypt. Tribal chiefs in southern Egypt (known as Upper Egypt) conquered the north (Lower Egypt), and the country was unified under the king, Narmer.

Pyramid Builders

Narmer founded the first of Egypt's dynasties of rulers.
The kings had absolute
authority in Egypt. The king was seen as the earthly
representative of Egypt's many gods, and was the link between them and his subjects.

During the period known as the Old Kingdom (2575–2134 BCE), the kings built huge stone pyramids as tombs.
The skills required to design and build the pyramids suggest the Egyptians had a high degree of scientific knowledge. Cutting the huge stone blocks, transporting them by river and assembling them also suggest an advanced level of social organisation. The government coordinated vast numbers of builders to provide labour.

Old Kingdom Egypt was centralised. The king took responsibility for feeding his subjects. In exchange, his subjects worked for the state, growing crops or working on large-scale building projects.

By the 6th Dynasty, local rulers began to seize power in their own areas. They challenged and eventually destroyed the absolute power of the king. From 2134 BCE, Egypt experienced a period of instability and social unrest known as the First Immediate Period.

The Middle Kingdom

Stability returned with the start of the Middle Kingdom in 2040 BCE. Egypt was reunited when Nebhepetre Mentuhotep II came to the throne.

The Mystery of the Pyramids

The oldest pyramids were built over 4,500 years ago. They were built as burial chambers for the Egyptian kings of the Old Kingdom, but how they were built remains a mystery. King Khufu's Great Pyramid at Giza contains more than 2.3 million limestone blocks, some of which weigh 15 tonnes (14.75 tons). How the builders got these huge blocks into position was also a puzzle for the Egyptians of the New Kingdom. By then, the pyramids were already ancient.

The Great Pyramids of Giza were built during the Old Kingdom. They remained the tallest structures on Earth until the late 19th century.

Word meanings

1. Find and copy a word in the text that means the same as a community of people living close to each other.

> When you answer questions about word meanings, think about the exact meaning of words within the context of the text.

....

1 mark

2. In the first paragraph, the River Nile is described as the 'lifeblood' of Egypt. Explain what this means.

....

.... **1 mark**

3. Read this extract from the text: 'The government coordinated vast numbers of builders.' Tick the box correctly describing the meaning of the word 'coordinated'.

Tick **one.**

asked ☐

distributed ☐

organised ☐

1 mark

4. Explain why *The Roots of the Empire* is a good title for this extract.

....

.... **2 marks**

5. Find and copy a word in the text that means the same as putting different parts together to make something.

.... **1 mark**

Inference about characters

1. Find and copy a phrase in *The Roots of the Empire* that tells you that Narmer held complete control over the Egyptian people.

   > Writers use inference to provide information about characters in an interesting way.

   .... 1 mark

2. Are the statements below true or false? Tick one box in each row. One has been done for you.

	true	false
The rulers of the Sixth Dynasty were obedient people.		✓
The rulers of the Sixth Dynasty were strong-willed people.		
The tribal chiefs of Upper Egypt were ambitious.		

   1 mark

3. Re-read the extract from *Stolen Destinies* on page 55. Circle the name of the country from which you think the narrator is mostly likely to have come originally. Give evidence for your answer.

   Spain   Scotland   Poland   Nigeria

   .... 2 marks

4. Read the last paragraph of the extract from *Stolen Destinies* on page 56. Tick the correct description of the narrator below.

                                                    Tick **one.**

   The narrator couldn't speak a word of Arabic. ☐

   The narrator was fluent in Arabic. ☐

   The narrator could speak some Arabic. ☐   1 mark

Summarising themes

1. Are the sentences below true or false?
   Use information from the text.

> Remember to read, understand and collate information from the text as a whole (rather than from individual sections).

	true	false
The Egyptians of the New Kingdom built the Pyramid of King Khufu.		
Pyramids were built to be used as palaces.		
King Narmer unified Egypt.		

1 mark

2. Draw lines to match the events to the period in which they happened.
   One has been done for you.

The first pyramids were built.	First Intermediate Period
King Nebhepetre Mentuhotep II was the ruler.	The Old Kingdom
A dynasty of rulers governed Egypt.	over 4,500 years ago
Egyptian society was unstable.	The Middle Kingdom

3 marks

3. What does *The Roots of the Empire* tell us about the skills and knowledge of Egyptian society under Narmer's rule?

   ....

   .... **2 marks**

4. In what ways do you think that the absolute authority of the kings might have been beneficial to Egyptian society? Use the text to support your answer.

   ....

   .... **2 marks**

Making comparisons

Some questions in the test ask you to compare different parts of information in the text to see how the information leads to the meaning as a whole.

1. In what way did Egyptian society change when it came under the rule of King Narmer and how did this change continue to effect civilisation?

....

.... 3 marks

2. How much knowledge did the Egyptians of the New Kingdom have of the pyramids of the Old Kingdom? Compare this knowledge to what is known about them today.

....

.... 2 marks

3. When did the First Intermediate Period occur, and how was Egyptian society different during this period than during the Old Kingdom?

....

....

.... 3 marks

4. In what chronological order did the following events take place? Number the sentences from 1 to 4 to show the correct order.

Nebhepetre Mentuhotep came to power.	
Small communities of people settled on the banks of the River Nile.	
The Great Pyramids were no longer the tallest structures on Earth.	
The Old Kingdom was destroyed.	

2 marks

Poems

I'm Not Scared

I'm not scared of vampire bats,
Growling wolves and hissing cats.
I'm not scared of snarling dogs,
Slippery slugs and jumping frogs,
And dancing shadows on the wall,
Well, they don't bother me at all!

I'm not scared of slimy snails,
Whistling winds and howling gales.
I'm not scared of trembling quakes,
Hairy spiders, hissing snakes,
And ferocious pirates in a crowd,
Well, they just make me laugh out loud!

I'm not scared of stinging bees,
Wriggly worms and itchy fleas.
I'm not scared of darkened rooms,
Cackling witches on their brooms,
And sharp-toothed monsters of the deep,
Well, they will send me off to sleep!

I'm not scared of grizzly bears,
Hospitals and dentist's chairs,
Hurricanes and lightning flashes,
Tornadoes, whirlwinds, thunder crashes.
None of these give me a fright,
But Mummy, don't turn out the light!

Gervase Phinn

On Port Meadow

That horse looks bigger than a sofa
And its nose is damp as a dish-cloth.
One minute it was over there, nibbling
grass,
And now it is here, nudging my
shoulder.

The wind is blowing the kites away
And lacing the surface of the
flooded field.
The seven horses who were minding
their own business
Are now over here, looking for
sugar-lumps.
It's no good laughing, and twisting
away
Like Blind-Man's-Bluff or a flamenco
dancer:
The horses are all round us, snorting,
And one of them has bitten my Mum's
bum.

John Fuller

Poem

What is the Pond Doing?

(for Ruairidh, who asked)

Wobbling like a wobbly jelly

Being a bucket for the rain

Sending flash-backs to the sun

Cheeking the sky

Giving the moon a bath

Letting swans, ducks and winter leaves ride on its back

Licking the lollipop reeds

Pretending to be soup for the wind to stir

Growing stinky skunk cabbages

Drawing wheels and circles then rubbing them out

Plopping slopping slurping spinning

Turning the weeping willows happily upside down

Dreaming of running away to sea

Hiding under a starry blanket of dark

What is the pond doing?

Ponding. Responding.

Diana Hendry

Reading poetry

Read the poem *I'm Not Scared* on page 70 and then answer the following questions.

1. Find and copy a word or phrase in the poem that means the same as:

   shaking rapidly   ....

   irritating to the skin   ....

   very fierce   ....   **3 marks**

2. Tick the box that best describes the main message in this poem.

   Tick **one**.

   Vampire bats can get into your bedroom. ☐
   It's normal for children to feel scared of the dark. ☐
   It's ridiculous to be afraid of the dark. ☐   **1 mark**

3. How does the poet create rhythm?

   ....

   ....

   ....   **2 marks**

4. How does the poet change the mood of the poem from the first line to the last?

   ....

   ....

   ....   **2 marks**

Alliteration

1. Read *I'm Not Scared* on page 70. Tick boxes to show which of the following phrases from the poem are examples of alliteration. Tick all that apply.

   scared of stinging ☐

   laugh out loud ☐

   trembling quakes ☐

   Slippery slugs ☐

   scared of snarling ☐

   vampire bats ☐

   > Alliteration is the repetition of a sound in words which are closely linked together.

   4 marks

2. Find and copy two more examples of alliteration used in *I'm Not Scared*.

   ....

   .... **2 marks**

3. Read *What Is the Pond Doing?* on page 71 and find and copy six examples of alliteration.

   ....

   ....

   .... **6 marks**

4. Explain how alliteration creates mood in a poem and makes a poem more powerful.

   ....

   ....

   .... **3 marks**

5. Write two sentences of your own, using alliteration to describe water.

   ....

   .... **2 marks**

73

Personification

1. Tick three boxes to show which of the following are examples of personification.

> Personification is when a writer gives human qualities or characteristics to an object or animal.

Tick **three**.

Smiling widely, the flower opened its petals and then beckoned to the bees. ☐

The rain splattered lightly against the window. ☐

Let determination take you by the hand and she will lead you to the top of the hill. ☐

The book was bursting with wise words it was dying to tell. ☐

3 marks

2. Read *On Port Meadow* on page 70. Find and copy one example of personification.

.... 1 mark

3. Read the poem *What Is the Pond Doing?* on page 71. The poet personifies the pond by attributing human actions to it, for example '*letting* the swans, ducks and winter leaves *ride* on its back'. Find and copy six more examples of personification in the poem.

....

....

.... 6 marks

4. What effect does the personification of the pond have on the reader?

....

.... 1 mark

5. Write two sentences of your own, using personification to describe water.

....

.... 2 marks

Onomatopoeia

1. Underline all the examples of onomatopoeia in the passage below.

> Onomatopoeia is when the sound of a word mimics the sound of the thing being described.

Dawn had just broken when Mrs Clement was woken up by a 'cuckoo' from the woods. There was such much to do on the farm. She was greeted by the yelping of the puppies and the barking of the large dogs in the kitchen. "Hush!" she said and banged their bowls of food down. The cat meowed as Mrs Clements fed her and then, putting on her wellingtons, she squelched out into the muddy farmyard.

It was full of noise: there was the hiss of the geese, the hee-haw of the donkey, the oink of the pigs, the baa of the sheep, the whinny of the pony in the stable and the cheeping and tweeting of the hens. By the time she had finished feeding all the animals she was exhausted. She sat down in the sunshine, yawned, slurped a cup of tea and listened to the buzzing of the bees. Within ten minutes she had fallen asleep and was snoring.

6 marks

2. Read *I'm Not Scared* on page 70. Find and copy two examples of onomatopoeia used in the poem.

....

.... 2 marks

3. Read *What Is the Pond Doing?* on page 71. Find and copy two examples of onomatopoeia used in the poem.

....

.... 2 marks

4. How does the use of onomatopoeia make a poem more effective?

....

.... 2 marks

Similes

1. Underline the similes in the passage below.

> Similes are phrases that directly compare two things. They often contain the word 'as' or 'like'.

> It was a monster of a day. Seventy-mile-an-hour winds lashed the hillside, felling mature trees like a deranged man with a giant axe. We ran outside to see, then dashed back in as a squall of rain drenched us. The electrical cables had been blown down so neither the lights nor the heating were working. We huddled inside the kitchen by the open fire trying to dry off, grinning in spite of the cold, like happy otters after an afternoon in the river.

2 marks

2. Read the poem *On Port Meadow* on page 70. Explain why the similes in the extract 'It's no good laughing, and twisting away, Like Blind-Man's Buff or a flamenco dancer.' are effective.

....

.... 2 marks

3. Find and copy two more examples of similes in *On Port Meadow* on page 70.

....

.... 2 marks

4. Complete the similes in the sentences below.

   a) The rabbit's fur was as soft as ....

   b) It is as sweet as ....

   c) His muscles are as hard as ....

3 marks

76

Metaphor

1. Underline the metaphors in the passage below.

   The leaves dance along the road, prancing, pirouetting and performing pique-turns. As light and graceful as prima ballerinas, their golden shades glittering in the crisp, October sunshine.

   Each of them is an autumnal jewel bedecking the pavement in any array of treasures.

   > A metaphor says that one thing is something else without using the words 'like' or 'as'.

   2 marks

2. Rewrite the metaphor 'Being a bucket for the rain' from *What Is the Pond Doing?* on page 71 as a simile.

   > Don't get confused between similes and metaphors. 'She is as fierce as a lioness' is a **simile**. Whereas, 'She is a fierce lioness' is a **metaphor**.

   .... **1 mark**

3. Read the first paragraph of *Stolen Destinies* on page 55. What metaphor does the writer use to describe the pattern of the sea behind the dhow?

   .... **1 mark**

4. In the second paragraph in the extract from *Stolen Destinies* on page 55 the writer uses the metaphor 'tide of fate' to describe the narrator's life. How is this image developed with another metaphor in the same paragraph?

   .... **1 mark**

Answers

GRAMMAR

1 Pronouns

1. **a)** She, him, they   **b)** Everyone, them, them   **c)** us
   d) He, himself

2. **b)** him **c)** her

3. Bashir and Jonathan set off for the bowling alley at five-thirty. The bus arrived at the stop at five- forty and **they** got on the bus. **They** were hoping to get to the bowling alley before six-thirty to make sure that **they** got a game but when **they** arrived **they** were disappointed to find that **it** was closed. **They** decided to go ice-skating instead.

2 Noun phrases

1. **a)** The guitarist performing on stage
   b) the supermarket, which sells great ice-cream
   c) The fat, floppy-eared puppy
   d) the boy with the spiky hair
   e) The copper-edged mirror

2. Examples:
   b) My cousins from Cheltenham didn't have enough money to catch the train.
   c) The greedy, fat cat was sitting on the window ledge watching the birds.
   d) Jackson delivered the pizza to the people living on the third floor.
   e) Malak met Naomi's younger sister by the tennis courts.
   f) The girl wearing the scarlet coat was walking towards us when it happened.

3 Possessive pronouns

1. **a)** Their   **b)** mine   **c)** hers   **d)** Your   **e)** his

2. **b)** Its collar was too big for it.
   c) Selma replaced all of his chocolates.
   d) His hips are causing him a lot of pain.
   e) Her car is brand new.

3. Example: Patrick's computer had been hacked.

4 Determiners

1. **b)** Many, his **c)** A , the
   d) All the, her **e)** This , the

3. We put the cat in the box, loaded her/him into the car and took her/him to a vet nearby.

5 Adjectives and adjectival phrases

1. Examples:
   a) cheerful **b)** tall **c)** ferocious

2. The train was going faster and faster.
   Those pancakes are extremely tasty.
   Scowling in anger, the man entered the room.

3. **a)** delicious, triple-chocolate-coated biscuits
   b) on the corner of the street

6 Verbs

1. <u>was</u>, <u>decided</u>, <u>wanted to go kayaking</u>, <u>made</u>, <u>renting</u>, <u>managed to rent</u>, <u>were</u>, <u>included</u>, <u>paddled</u>, <u>returned</u>, <u>were aching</u>. <u>Shall we go</u>, <u>asked</u>, <u>let's</u>, <u>do</u>, weather's, <u>replied</u>

2. **a)** were **b)** am not **c)** were **d)** hasn't

3. a word used to talk about an action in the past, present or future

7 Present and past tense

1. Alfred was born in 1920.

2. Khalid **had** two brothers and a sister. His sister **had** shoulder-length, brown hair and **liked** playing netball. She **played** for her school team and **was** the captain. His brothers **were** identical twins and **were** two years younger than him. All the children in Khalid's family **had** inherited their mothers' green eyes.

3. Example: 'Catches' is used because it describes something she does every day and is routine and 'is walking' describes an action she is taking now.

8 Future tense

1. They're going to have salad and pizza for dinner this evening. The programme that you want to watch will be broadcast at seven o'clock. We're leaving for the airport soon.

2. will be engineered, will run, we are going, will be brought, will face, will be, is launching.

9 Modal verbs

1. **a)** would **b)** shall **c)** must **d)** may

2. certainty, possibility, possibility, possibility, certainty

3. We might go to the party if we get back in time. → It might happen. I will catch the ten o'clock bus. → It will definitely happen. Unless it stops raining the barbecue will be cancelled. → It is unlikely to happen. He will not be able to make it. → It definitely won't happen.

10 Present and past perfect tense

1. The timetable had begun before the new head teacher arrived.

2. **a)** had been invented **b)** has spilt **c)** had been taken

3. Examples: **a)** She has left her bag here by mistake.
   b) It had rained all night so the ground was soaked.

4. To talk about an event in the past which still has consequences now.

11 Future perfect tense

1. By the time you are twelve years old you will have started secondary school.

2. **b)** She wants to make sure the meal has been prepared before the guests arrive.
   c) Ben will have completed the marathon before any of the other runners have started.
   d) If he keeps eating so much junk food he will become very fat before he grows up.

3. Example: To show that by the time something happens in the future another event will already have taken place.

12 Adverbs

1. hard, early, very fast, carefully, accurately, correctly, enthusiastically, happily

3. **b)** Toby speaks quietly. **c)** Caitlin paints beautifully.
   d) Grandma sleeps badly.

13 Adverbial phrases

1. **a)** by the light of the moon **b)** Before the end of the week **c)** over the bridge **d)** So that I won't forget
   e) during the interval **f)** to make sure I woke up on time

2. Out of the corner of my eye, I spotted the wallet. With great regret, the teacher announced that he was leaving. Speaking quickly, she explained what had happened.

3. Examples: **a)** We went to see the film that everyone was talking about.
   b) After the clock struck midnight, Cinderella ran home.

14 Conjunctions

1. **b)** until (subordinating conjunction) **c)** because (subordinating conjunction) **d)** but (co-ordinating conjunction)

2. Examples: **a)** The bottle was empty so we put it in the recycling bin. **b)** The puppy chews shoes but it is still adorable. **c)** We arrived on time although we left the house late.

3. after, because, when, while, although

4. Coordinating conjunctions join together two main clauses or compound sentences.

15 Prepositions

1. **b)** before **c)** at **d)** on **e)** into

2. direction, place, time, place, time, place

3. Examples: The film is shown on Saturdays.
   The garage is beside the house.
   The rabbits ran into the woods.

16 Prepositional phrases

1. **b)** around the bend **c)** by the light of the moon **d)** after many attempts **e)** until this very day

2. time, direction, place

3. Examples: **a)** On the count of ten the racers set off.
   b) They ate lunch in the centre of the mall.
   c) The children ran around the playing field.

17 Subjunctive

1. **a)** complete **b)** be approved **c)** undergo **d)** apologise **e)** arrive **f)** check

2. Examples: **a)** It is advised that overweight patients lose weight by following a sensible diet.
   b) I insist that you do as I say.
   c) The weather is dreadful so I urge you to drive carefully.
   d) It's nearly tea-time so I recommend that we go home.
   e) I don't think that he should come.

3. Example: It is recommended that passengers check in at least two hours before departure.

4. Examples: The subjunctive is used to emphasis importance or urgency. The subjunctive is also used to talk about something that hasn't happened or is uncertain.

18 Questions

1. How could this possibly happen? Would you prefer tomatoes or peppers with your steak? She's quite tall, isn't she?

2. **a)** isn't it? **b)** isn't she? **c)** are they? **d)** hasn't she?

3. Examples: Who is the man with dark hair? What time does the party start? When are you going on holiday?

4. Examples: Have they done their homework? Do they want to go to the park? Will you help me make a cake?

19 Commands and exclamations

1. command, exclamation, command, exclamation, command.

2. Quick! Go and phone the police!
   Boil the rice for ten minutes then rinse it in hot water.

3. **a)** It must contain the question word 'what' or 'how' and a verb. It must contain an exclamation mark.
   b) To express surprise or a command.

4. Example: Join the two sides as shown in the instructions.

20 Subject and object

1. **b)** Yusif **c)** They **d)** The wheel barrow **e)** A cat

2. **a)** bread **b)** dog **c)** day out
   d) mouse **e)** cheese **f)** ink

3. Example: Freddy gave the chocolate to his little brother.

4. a subject, a verb

21 Phrases and clauses

1. phrase, clause, phrase, clause, phrase

2. **a)** Until final completion **b)** broken into a thousand pieces **c)** Before sitting the test **d)** smoke pouring from its exhaust

3. Example: A phrase is a collection of words that may have nouns or verbs but does not have a subject doing something. A clause is also a group of words. It has a subject that is actively doing something.

4. Examples:
   a) The lady at the checkout, who is wearing a yellow uniform, is my aunt.
   b) Yawning sleepily, the toddler settled down in his bed.

22 Main and subordinate clauses

1. subordinate, main, main, subordinate

2. **a)** Since his dog died **b)** while she listened to the radio
   c) even though she goes to the gym twice a week
   d) Despite the fact that he was very angry

3. Example: He drank the juice because he was thirsty.

4. Example: A main clause could be used as a complete sentence. A subordinate clause only makes sense when it used alongside a main clause.

23 Compound and complex sentences

1. complex, compound, compound, complex

2. Examples: **a)** because **b)** Although **c)** and **d)** but

3. a co-ordinating conjunction

4. A complex sentence is formed by one main clause and one or more subordinate clauses. A compound sentence is formed by two main clauses connected by a coordinating conjunction.

24 Relative clauses

1. who, which, whosoever, that, whose

2. **b)** which is securely locked after school **c)** whose friend works in London **d)** which was squawking in the cage **e)** when a date has been set

3. **a)** who **b)** where **c)** which **d)** whose

4. Example: That girl, who is jumping on the trampoline, is my sister's friend.

25 Active and passive voice

1. active, passive, passive, active, passive

2. **b)** The luggage was left in the storage area by them.
   c) The parcel has been delivered by the post woman.
   d) All the grass in the paddock is eaten by the horses.
   e) The clothes are being hung on the line by him.

3. Example: When we want to sound more formal (such as in written reports). To avoid blaming or accusing someone of something.

4. Example: The ice-cream was eaten by the children.

Answers

26 Standard English verbs

1. It is regrettable that he has chosen to ignore everyone's advice on this matter. Please ensure that all litter is collected and placed in the bins provided.

2. b) He was at school yesterday.
   c) They were finishing their homework.
   d) We were waiting in the queue.

3. writing a letter to your local fire station to ask if your school could visit, applying for a Saturday job helping out in a pet shop

27 Standard English tense and voice

1. a) incorrect, correct, correct, incorrect
   b) The bikes were left near the station.
      The lawn was mowed by the gardener.

2. b) The church was built in 1786.
   c) The burgers were cooked to perfection in time for the barbecue.

3. Example: Dear Mrs Jones, I would be grateful if you could allow me an extra day in which to complete my homework. I did finish it last night and left it on a low table. Unfortunately it was chewed by the dog. I apologise and hope that you will be able to allow me a further day.
   Yours sincerely

28 Standard English grammar

1. The concert is scheduled to commence at seven o'clock. We attended our grandmother's eightieth birthday celebration.

2. a) I completed my homework promptly.
   b) It was a pleasure to meet you.
   c) Those peaches look delicious.

3. informal, formal

4. Example: I will be going to the cinema with my friend Ashling tomorrow.

PUNCTUATION

29 Commas for clarity

1. a) The table was set with a buffet of jelly, sausage rolls, ice-cream, burgers and walnut salad.
   b) The teacher told us to put our bags under our desks, take out our PE kit, get changed and then line up outside the gym.
   c) You need to pack a sleeping bag, a ground sheet, a water bottle and warm clothes.
   d) While you're at the shop buy bread, cheese, milk and a bunch of grapes.

2. a) Uncle Stanley, who has worked at the factory for twenty-five years, will retire soon.
   b) Although it was very late, the sky was still illuminated.
   c) Mina, who you met when we were skiing, loves pasta.
   d) Despite being quite small, Nathaniel is very strong.
   e) Even though you're not keen on cheese, you should still try the pizza.

3. I love: eating, my friends, my grandmother and skate boarding.

4. Example: To clarify meaning and avoid ambiguity.

30 Parenthesis

1. The indoor market was a hive of activity, filled with people everywhere, with stalls piled high with goods for sale.

2. a) (who speaks three languages) b) (which hangs above the fireplace) c) (where we spent the weekend)

3. Examples: a) next to the station, b) who was very shy, c) who likes peace and quiet, d) which had springs sticking out of it.

4. Example: To insert additional information within an already complete sentence.

31 Colons

1. At the supermarket we bought: six eggs, half a kilo of oranges, chocolate and ham.

2. a) In my locker I keep: extra pens, books, a bar of chocolate and my rugby boots.
   b) To train for a marathon you need to: do warm-up exercises, run six miles a day and eat a healthy diet.

3. a) The television presenter announced: "We have just received the breaking news that a spaceship with six Martians has landed on Earth."
   b) Albert Einstein said: "Look deeper into nature and then you will understand everything better."

4. a) Example: My brother is taking ten GCSEs: Maths, English, Drama, Music, Art, Chemistry, Biology, French, Spanish and Latin.
   b) Example: Shakespeare wrote: "Love all, trust a few, do wrong to none."

32 Semi-colons

1. Nathan has been working out every day; he's getting very fit now. The hurricane caused tremendous damage: broken windows; dislodged tiles; up-rooted trees; disconnected power lines and the destruction of gardens.

2. a) The garden is filled with a huge variety of plants: exquisite trailing roses; lilac-blossomed wisteria; scarlet hibiscus and wild foxgloves.
   b) The wildlife safari park keeps many different types of interesting animals: red wolves; roaring lions; Siberian tigers; lively-eyed lemurs and long-limbed giraffes.
   c) She is a huge fan of that pop star; she has an extensive collection of his music.

3. To separate items in a long list of items.

33 Possessive apostrophes

1. The women's toilet has got beautiful porcelain hand basins and scented soap.

2. a) Sophie's b) children's c) boys' d) Tom's

3. b) Herbert's sweatshirt is filthy.
   c) Our neighbours' driveway is close to ours.
   d) Jamal's car is very smart.
   e) The children's school is in the centre of town.

34 Apostrophes for contractions

1. She hasn't visited Scotland for four years.

2. b) We haven't lived here for long.
   c) It's convenient that the bus leaves from the end of our street.

3. a) He has not been able to spare the time to complete the form.
   b) They would not accept this proposal under any circumstances.

4. It'll, couldn't, they're, can't

80

35 Direct speech

1. "Where have all the apricots gone?" asked Deanna.
2. **b)** "We've won the competition!" shouted Donal.
   c) "Does it ever stop raining in this country?" asked Bridget gloomily.
   d) "Help! All the chickens have escaped!"
3. Example: "Shall we go to the beach on Saturday afternoon?" whispered Lily. "Yes, let's do that," whispered back Tao. "Roll on the weekend," they both sighed aloud.

36 Bullet points

1. false, true, true, false
2. In order to fully qualify as a doctor you need to:
   • be interested in biology
   • gain high grades at school
   • study at university for five years
   • work long hours in hospitals while you are training.
3. Example: Good teachers are always:
   • patient
   • caring
   • fair
   • clear in their instructions.

37 Hyphens and ellipses

1. hyphen, ellipsis, hyphen, hyphen.
2. **a)** one-way **b)** Ready-made **c)** left-handed **d)** red-hot
3. To show a word or text has been left out.
   To create suspense in a piece of writing.

SPELLING

38 Prefixes

1. disrespectful, unqualified, immature, irregular, misbehave
2. **a)** unfortunate **b)** retake **c)** subway **d)** irresponsible **e)** previews
3. Examples: incapable, autopilot, unable
4. To change the meaning of a root word.

39 Suffixes

1. eldest, started, taking, driving, nervous, assured, careful, driver, instructor, cheerful, brightly, coloured
2. **b)** careless **c)** hopeless **d)** admiration **e)** advantageous
3. suddenly, comfortable, contentment, dangerous

40 Synonyms and antonyms

1. cruelty → kindness, inflate → deflate, textured → smooth, responsible → irresponsible
2. Examples: **a)** huge **b)** delicious **c)** stared **d)** worried
3. quarrel and argue

41 Tricky spellings: silent letters

1. lambs, Tuesday, centre, climbed, castle, while, Christof, castle, ghost, knew, laugh, Christof, knack, laugh, lambs, knocked, gnome, knuckles
2. Examples:

knock	wrist	chemist	where
knew	wrong	mechanic	when
knob	wreck	ache	whether

3. Example: I was nervous in the exam even though I <u>knew</u> the <u>answers</u>.

42 Tricky spellings: pronunciation

1. Examples: 'ei': receive, ceiling, receipt, protein, seize
   'ie': achieve, mischief, piece, brief, priest
2. Examples: thought, bought
3. <u>cheef</u>, <u>recieved</u>, <u>siezed</u>, <u>breif</u>, <u>acheivement</u>
   chief, received, seized, brief, achievement

43 Homophones and homonyms

1. bare, loan, mail, sleigh, hear
2. Examples: **b)** Put your <u>coat</u> on it's cold.
   c) There's a great <u>band</u> playing in the community centre tonight.
   d) The beaches along that <u>coast</u> are lovely and sandy.
   e) The assistant placed the jar of sweets on the <u>counter</u>.
3. Homophones are pairs of words that sound the same but are spelled differently. Homonyms are pairs of words that sound the same and are also spelled the same.

WRITING

44 Audience and purpose

1. advice on travelling to Japan → a tourist, instructions to assemble flat-pack furniture → a customer of a DIY store, a science fiction novel → someone who likes stories about space and time travel, a history textbook → a school pupil
2. The intended audience is a reader of a fiction story set in the past and the purpose is to entertain.
3. Answer to use a polite, friendly style with correct grammar, punctuation and spelling.

45 Planning and organising

1. Examples: what you want to say, how you are going to say it, how you are going to set it out and correct paragraph formatting
2. Answer to include appropriate notes in each section.
3. Answer to include demonstration of awareness of constructing a story using a well-thought out plan.

46 Drafting and improving

1. Examples: adjectives, adverbs, similes, correction of spelling and paragraphs.
2. Answer to include appropriate literary devices, correct punctuation and clear paragraphing.
3. Examples: to correct any spelling or punctuation errors, to improve writing for clarity and to add interest

47 Proof-reading

1. The Secret Maze
   My dad and I, countryside, weekend, an, parked, Which, first?", "There's, "Let's, garden," **fountain, whole, were, edge, spotted, leads** "Let's, We, through, were, maze.
2. Examples: incorrect spelling, omission of 'an' in front of word beginning with a vowel, omission of a capital letter, incorrect use of speech marks, incorrect subject/verb agreement, missing punctuation

Answers

48 Writing stories

1. Examples: an interesting title, an intriguing first line, effective adjectives and adverbs, good use of similes and metaphors, inference to give information about characters and events, a well thought out plot with a beginning, a middle and an end

2. Examples: an interesting title, an intriguing first line, use of similes, use of metaphor, inference to provide information about character and event

3. Answers to include a selection of the following: an interesting title, an intriguing first line, effective adjectives and adverbs, good use of similes and metaphors, inference to give information about characters and events, a well thought out plot with a beginning, a middle and an end

49 Persuasive writing

1. Examples: marketing or publicity material, a newspaper article giving a particular opinion, a leaflet from a political party

2. uses emotive language, has an opening sentence that hooks the reader, has a catchy title

3. Answer to include demonstration of awareness of persuasive writing strategies.

50 Instructions and reports

1. The match was scheduled to commence at two o'clock.

2. Example: Shore Primary were beaten 2-8 by Northcourt Primary at the inter-school netball championships last Saturday. This was a disappointing score for Shore Primary in view of their reputation as last year's overall champions. Luck wasn't on Shore's side this time though. Their wing-attacker, Aliyah Thomson, was taken off before the end of the first quarter. Shore's goal-shooter, Keiko Phillips, was on her usual good form but Northcourt's new goal defence, Phoebe Williams, stopped all except two of the goals. Northcourt and Shore will play against each other again on April 22nd.

3. Example: 1 Plump up pillows. 2 Check bottom sheet is tucked in. 3 Pull up duvet to cover the bed. 4. Smooth down the duvet.

51 Formal letters

1. Yours sincerely, I look forward to hearing from you at your earliest convenience, If the manager were able to meet me that would be very valuable, Please give my kind regards to your father.

2. Answer to demonstrate the correct formatting and appropriate use of Standard English.

52 Informal letters

1. false, true, false, false

2. Answer to demonstrate the correct formatting and appropriate use of informal language.

READING

53 Reading skills: close meaning

1. Morning or late morning. "I thought I'd let you sleep in. You had a big day yesterday."

2. '(she claimed)'

3. Because she is lying to him.

4. Example: The road isn't where very wealthy people live. It's just an ordinary place.

54 Reading skills: the whole text

1. Example: Alfie's dad has joined up to the army. His mother and grandmother are very upset.

2. Example: Margie is shocked and sad by Georgie joining up to the army. She is fearful of what might happen to him at war.

3. Example: Alfie is confused by his father's appearance but also impressed. Margie is shaken, angry and sad. Georgie is resigned to his duty and Granny Summerfield is shocked and stunned.

57 Retrieving information

1. It was calm. Examples: 'The torpid sea stretched sleepily to the horizon.' 'Its satin surface was undisturbed but for the ship's marbled wake…'

2. He could smell the spices. 3. He's a doctor.

4. He knows hardly anything at all. 5. frankincense

58 Recording information: selecting an answer

1. friendly, intuitive 2. an old man

3. true, false 4. excited

59 Recording information: free answers

1. 'my stubbly chin'

2. No. Example: Because he says 'Even if all I have left of this lifetime are these memories I would not barter these tender treasures for Jason's Golden Fleece.'

3. Example: It tells us that he is now old and quite lonely and unhappy.

4. Example: I think he is an adventurous and outgoing person who loves travelling to new places because he is very excited about arriving in Muscat. He says 'I'd been waiting for this moment for many months'.
I think he's also a friendly person who gets on with other people because he is good friends with Ahmed. He talks about an 'easy companionship'.

60 Using evidence

1. Example: I think it is very hot and sunny with very little rain. We know this because the narrator is sun-burned and he is very thirsty. The text also refers to desert sands.

2. No, he is not married. The text describes him as having 'no loving wife'.

3. a) a remote and undiscovered land
   b) 'shifting sands of The Empty Quarter'

4. 'His Highness Bin Taimur, Sultan and absolute ruler of the Kingdom of Muscat'

5. 'From these shores the Queen of Sheba had dispatched ships heavy with frankincense. The legendary lost city of Ubar was said to lie beneath the shifting sands of the Empty Quarter to the south. 'The Atlantis of the Sands' was how it had been described by Lawrence of Arabia.'

61 Inference

1. a) an old man   b) 'yellowing teeth', 'gnarled fingers'

2. Because he wants to explore the desert and discover the lost city of Ubar. We know because he talks about finding 'fabulous hoards of jewels and artefacts'. He is also taking a job with the British Consulate.

3. Example: I think Ahmed is much shorter than the narrator. I know this because it says he reached up to slap the narrator across the shoulders and that he was a 'slightly built chap'.

4. Example: No, because they drank water from a goatskin bag.

62 Prediction

1. Example: When he was young he thought he knew everything but he didn't really. Things are going to happen to him that will make him realise this.

2. Example: It would suggest that he will never leave because important events will happen that will keep him there. 'Had I known that having once set foot on the burning rocks of that enchanted land I was starting a voyage from which there could be no return?'

3. Example: Yes, I think they will stay friends because they have formed a good friendship already. Ahmed slaps the narrator on the shoulders and shares his goatskin water bag with him so they must be close.

63 Authors' language

1. a feeling of heat and sleepiness and a very calm, hot day with a flat sea and no wind 2. personification

3. Example: 'My pulse quickened. I'd been waiting for this moment for many months…'

4. Example: rocky cliffs that look like castles with turrets

5. alliteration

66 Word meanings

1. settlement

2. Example: It means that the river kept the people alive by providing fish and water to grow crops and food.

3. organised

4. Example: Because the text describes the history of the empire and what it grew from.

5. 'assembling'

67 Inference about characters

1. 'absolute authority' 2. true, true

3. Scotland, 'My Celtic skin was raw'

4. The narrator could speak some Arabic.

68 Summarising themes

1. false, false, true

2. The first pyramids were built. → over 4,500 years ago, A dynasty of rulers governed Egypt. → The Old Kingdom, Egyptian society was unstable. → First Intermediate Period

3. Example: It tells us that the people had advanced skills and a high degree of scientific knowledge.

4. Example: It provided stability. 'The king took responsibility for feeding his subjects.'

69 Making comparisons

1. Example: Before King Narmer came to power Egypt was ruled by different tribal chiefs. Narmer unified the country under his rule. This was the start of several centuries of governance under the absolute authority of several dynasties of kings.

2. Example: The Egyptians of the New Kingdom didn't have any more knowledge of how the pyramids of the Old Kingdom were built than we have today. It was also a puzzle to them.

3. Example: The First Intermediate Period occurred when local rulers seized power from the king and destroyed his absolute authority. This brought about a period of unrest.

4. 3, 1, 4, 2

72 Reading poetry

1. trembling quakes, itchy fleas, ferocious

2. It's normal for children to feel scared of the dark.

3. By using rhyming couplets.

4. In the first line and most of the poem the child is full of bravado and says that he or she is not afraid of anything. However in the last line he or she is very honest and admits to being afraid of the dark.

73 Alliteration

1. scared of snarling, laugh out loud, slippery slugs, scared of stinging

2. scared of slimy snails, whistling winds

3. wobbling like a wobbly jelly, licking the lollipop, stinky skunk, slopping slurping spinning, weeping willows, Ponding Responding

4. Alliteration is used in poetry to create different effects with the repetition of letter or syllable sounds, either for a description or to create more excitement or danger.

5. Examples: The drops of dripping water drained away. The blustery, billowing waves bounced onto the beach.

74 Personification

1. Smiling widely, the flower opened its petals and then beckoned to the bees. Let determination take you by the hand and she will lead you to the top of the hill. The book was bursting with wise words it was dying to tell.

2. The seven horses who were minding their own business.

3. Examples: Sending flash-backs to the sun, Cheeking the sky, Giving the moon a bath, Licking the lollipop reeds, Pretending to be soup for the wind to stir, Growing stinky skunk cabbages

4. Example: It makes the reader feel affection and sympathy for the pond as if the pond were a person. It makes the reader feel appreciative of ponds and nature.

5. Examples: The calm and glistening water invited me in. The waterfall shouted loudly as it fell against the rocks.

75 Onomatopoeia

1. 'cuckoo', yelping, barking, "Hush!", banged, meowed, squelched

hiss, hee-haw, oink, baa, whinny, cheep, tweeting, yawned slurped, buzzing, snoring

2. Examples: growling, hissing, snarling, whistling, howling, hissing, cackling, crashes

3. Examples: wobbling, plopping, slopping, slurping

4. Example: Onomatopoeia is a device that writers and poets can use to create a more powerful atmosphere by using the sense of sound that is sometimes difficult to express with words alone.

76 Similes

1. like a deranged man with a giant axe, like happy otters after an afternoon in the river

2. Example: It is effective because it conveys the lively twisting, escaping movement that you make when horses crowd round you.

3. The horse looks bigger than a sofa. And its nose is damp as a dish-cloth.

4. Examples:
a) velvet b) sugar c) iron

77 Metaphor

1. leaves dance, prancing, pirouetting, performing pique-turns
Each of them is an autumnal jewel

2. Example: The pond was like a bucket for the rain.

3. 'marbled wake'

4. 'It was an undercurrent too strong for me to ever have swum against.'

Published by Pearson Education Limited, 80 Strand, London, WC2R 0RL.

www.pearsonschools.co.uk

Text © Pearson Education Limited 2016
Edited by Jane Cotter
Typeset by Jouve India Private Limited
Produced by Elektra Media
Original illustrations © Pearson Education Limited 2016
Illustrated by Elektra Media
Cover illustration by Ana Albero

The right of Helen Thomson to be identified as author of this work has been asserted by her in accordance with the Copyright, Designs and Patents Act 1988.

First published 2016

19 18 17 16
10 9 8 7 6 5 4 3 2 1

British Library Cataloguing in Publication Data
A catalogue record for this book is available from the British Library.

ISBN 978 1 292 14598 3

Printed in Slovakia by Neografia

Acknowledgements

We are grateful to the following for permission to reproduce copyright material:

Text
Extracts on pages 53 and 54 from *Stay Where You Are And Then Leave* Random House (Boyne, J.).
Extracts on pages 53 and 54 from *Stay Where You Are and Then Leave* Henry Holt and Co. (Boyne, J.).
Print rights for US and Canada. Extract on pages 64–65 from *The Egyptian Empire*, Hachette
Children's Group c/o Wayland Books (Roxburgh, E. 2015). Poetry on page 70 from *Michael Rosen's A to Z, The Best Children's Poetry from Agard to Zephaniah* (Fuller, J.), "On Port Meadow".
Poetry on page 70 from *The Day Our Teacher Went Batty*, Puffin (Phinn, G. 2002), "I'm Not Scared".
© Gervase Phinn. Poetry on page 71 from *Michael Rosen's A to Z, The Best Children's Poetry from Agard to Zephaniah* (Hendry, D.), "What is the Pond Doing?".

Picture credits
The publisher would like to thank the following for their kind permission to reproduce their photographs:

Alamy Images: Jeremy Moeran 70; **Shutterstock.com:** Kurt Pacaud 71, WitR 65

All other images © Pearson Education